And then the full realisation of what had been happening, of what could so easily have happened, of what she had been *wanting* to happen, struck suddenly into her mind. And she jerked herself out of his arms, staring at him with all her old panic in her eyes.

'Cassa! Don't look like that—I'm not going to hurt you——'

'You're not going to do *anything* to me!' she exclaimed, putting several feet of space between them with one spring. 'I don't know what I was thinking of——'

'I do!' he interrupted, grinning.

'I must have gone mad—there's a full moon somewhere—I was out of my mind—it meant nothing, *nothing*.' She backed against the old wall, feeling the rough stones like reality under her hands. 'You understand that, don't you, Jet. It meant nothing—and it's never going to happen again.'

We hope you're enjoying our new addition to our Contemporary Romance series—stories which take a light-hearted look at the Zodiac and show that love can be written in the stars!

Every month you can get to know a different combination of star-crossed lovers, with one story that follows the fortune of a hero and heroine when they embark on the romance of a lifetime with somebody born under another sign of the Zodiac. This month features a sizzling love-affair between **Aquarius** and **Gemini**.

To find out more fascinating facts about this month's featured star sign, turn to the back pages of this book. . .

ABOUT THIS MONTH'S AUTHOR

Nicola West says: 'I was born on the fourth of July under the sign of Cancer—which makes me a shy, secretive homemaker! I've got over the shyness now—though it was crippling when I was younger—but although I have a lot of good friends—and enjoy being with them—I do also enjoy solitude. I certainly like to make a home for myself and my family, though I'm by no means a houseproud wife; I love to feed people and enjoy cooking meals for friends, but—since I prefer to spend my time with them, rather than in the kitchen—I like to have as much organised as possible beforehand.

Writing ENIGMA MAN introduced me to the world of crystals, and I am learning more about this fascinating subject.

ENIGMA MAN

BY

NICOLA WEST

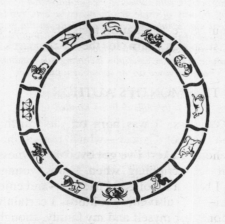

MILLS & BOON LIMITED
ETON HOUSE   18–24 PARADISE ROAD
RICHMOND   SURREY   TW9 1SR

First published in Great Britain 1992
by Mills & Boon Limited

© Nicola West 1992

Australian copyright 1992
Philippine copyright 1992
This edition 1992

ISBN 0 263 77406 6

STARSIGN ROMANCES is a trademark of Harlequin Enterprises
B.V., Fribourg Branch. Mills and Boon is an authorised user.

Set in 10 on 12 pt Linotron Times
01-9201-55786 Z
Typeset in Great Britain by Centracet, Cambridge
Made and printed in Great Britain

With thanks to Ursula Markham

CHAPTER ONE

The woman noticed her eyes still ... be crystals
that Cassa had spread before her. They ... ly gleaming crystals of all kinds—rose and ... ... crystals,
agates, jaspers, bloodstones, and lapis—a bewildering

CHAPTER ONE

THE priory clock was just striking twelve, its deep tones booming across the hilly little town, when Jet Tayler walked into Cassa Newton's crystal shop.

Cassa was busy helping a customer to choose a crystal, and did not look up immediately. Her first glance had shown her that the newcomer was accompanied by her father's old friend James Meakin, and he had smiled and lifted a hand to indicate that she must not break off from her work. Not that Cassa had any intention of doing so. Helping someone to choose a crystal was far too important, especially when it was their first.

'Just let your feelings tell you which to choose,' she encouraged the woman who was gazing entranced at the tray of stones. 'Close your eyes for a moment or two and when you open them see if one of the stones is brighter than the others. Try handling them—one might feel warmer than the others, or it might even tingle in your hand. Or just close your eyes again and move your hands very gently over the crystals, not touching them.' She smiled at the bemused face. 'There's no hurry,' she said gently. 'One of these crystals is yours, and it won't let you go away without it.'

The woman nodded, her eyes still on the crystals that Cassa had spread before her. They lay softly gleaming, crystals of all kinds—rose and quartz crystals, agates, jaspers, bloodstones amethysts—a bewildering

7

choice which must seem almost impossible. But a choice would be made. Of that Cassa was quite sure.

It would probably be a good idea at this point to leave her customer to try the various methods of making her choice. Cassa moved quietly away and went over to the case where James and his companion were looking at some silver jewellery.

'Very attractive,' the stranger was saying. He turned at Cassa's approach and looked down at her. 'Very attractive indeed. . .' His voice deepened at the words and the slate-grey of his eyes turned a darker, warmer hue. He seemed for a moment to look straight into Cassa's mind, and she felt a sudden warmth flood her skin.

'Hello, James,' she said quickly, turning to the older man. 'Nice to see you. Have you heard from Mum and Dad lately? I had a letter on Monday—they were asking after you.'

'Yes, I heard too.' He smiled behind his beard, brown eyes twinkling. 'All the way from Australia— they seem to be having a wonderful time.'

'Oh, they are. They're loving being there with Brian and Jean and the children. In fact, I'm beginning to wonder if they'll ever come back!'

'Oh, they'll come back,' Professor Meakin said. 'They couldn't abandon Malvern for long—nor their lovely daughter. They'll be back soon enough, just to see what mischief you're getting up to!'

Cassa laughed, and then glanced again at the stranger. He was looking at her with the same intent gaze that had already brought a blush to her cheeks. She wondered who he could be. He didn't look like James Meakin's usual kind of acquaintance, although she found it hard to say why. Tall—something over six feet, she guessed—with hair the rich golden-brown of an eagle's wing and those shimmering grey eyes; there was an aura about him of wildness, of something untamed. She stepped fractionally away, not wanting to be too close, yet that felt wrong too. She looked at her father's friend.

James Meakin didn't seem to notice anything amiss. 'Let me introduce you to Jet Tayler,' he said easily. 'He wasn't a student of mine, but we had quite a lot to do with each other while I was at Cambridge. Of course, he's led a dissolute sort of life since then— quite reprehensible, in fact—but he does seem to be settling down now. Or so he says!'

The two men looked at each other, grinning, and Jet Tayler turned to Cassa and held out his hand. She looked at it, hesitating for a moment, feeling almost as if by taking it she would be making a decision, stepping into a world she wasn't sure she wanted to enter. She felt almost as if she were being manoeuvred in some way, pushed. . .but that was ridiculous. It was an introduction, nothing more.

She laid her hand in Jet Tayler's and immediately withdrew it again. That tingling! It was the feeling she had advised her customer to notice when choosing her crystal, the sensation Cassa herself had often experienced when choosing a new stone for herself. But Jet Tayler wasn't a stone, for heaven's sake! And she certainly wasn't choosing him, not in any way.

She glanced up into his eyes again and saw the same darkening that had disturbed her a few moments ago. A shiver ran over her skin.

'Cassa's parents are in Australia at the moment,' Professor Meakin was saying, and she realised that he must have already told Jet her name, 'staying with her brother and his family. Brian's several years older than Cassa, of course.'

'And is this their shop?' Jet asked politely. 'I see the name Newton over the door.'

'No, it's my shop,' Cassa replied. 'Are you staying in Malvern long, Mr Tayler?'

'Oh, Jet, please.' He grinned and she responded automatically. He really did have a very attractive smile, with those white teeth and glinting eyes. Not handsome, she decided, but certainly a man most women would turn to look at. If only he didn't have that strange effect on her.

'I don't really know how long I'll be around,' he was saying now. 'A few weeks at least. I'm doing some research for a book I'm writing, and James here is showing me around a little.' He looked down from his considerable height. 'He thought you might be able to help me a bit.'

'Me? How could I help you with a book?' But she felt a quiver of pleasure at the thought. Cassa loved books and had always wished she could write. Helping with one would be a good substitute—but how on earth. . .? 'I don't know anything about it,' she said quickly, and Jet laughed. He had a nice laugh too.

'I don't want you to help me write it! But you may have some local knowledge that would be extremely useful. James tells me that you——' He turned quickly as Cassa's customer gave a sudden exclamation. 'I'm sorry, I'm disrupting your work.'

Cassa gave him a brief smile and hurried to the customer's aid. The woman's hand was resting on the table, palm upwards, and nestling in it was a small, shining amethyst. The woman was almost quivering with excitement.

'It's this one,' she said. 'This one. It *told* me—it seemed to call me, somehow. It's as if—as if it's been waiting for me—I can't explain. . .'

Cassa smiled at the excitement on her face. 'I know exactly what you mean. It's your crystal, there's no doubt about it. I told you one of them would be, didn't I? Now, let me wrap it for you.' She took the crystal, amused and pleased to see that the woman was almost reluctant to give it up. It was always a satisfying moment when she knew that a customer had chosen the right crystal. She glanced up for a moment and caught Jet Tayler's eyes on her, and smiled with the pure pleasure of achievement.

But Jet didn't smile back. And she felt the chill of knowing he was a sceptic. Her moment of pleasure evaporated as if it had never been.

'There you are,' she said to the woman, trying hard to recapture the bond between them. 'Take it home now and cleanse it under running water, and then charge it. Then it will have all your positive energies and you'll be able to use it.'

'How do I do that?' the customer asked doubtfully, taking the wrapped crystal back.

'Charge it? Well, sit in a chair, holding the crystal in your hands, and think of a beautiful scene. Imagine a spiral of white light winding clockwise around you——' she was conscious of Jet's eyes fixed sardonically on her and felt a spurt of irritation, but ploughed steadily on '—and then your crystal will be ready to work for you. And I hope you enjoy it.'

'Oh, I will,' the woman said earnestly. 'I know I will. Thank you *so* much.'

She hurried out, cradling the wrapped crystal in her

hands, and Cassa watched her go, her pleasure returning. Then she remembered Jet Tayler and turned back
with a small sigh.

'Well done,' he commented drily. 'You make an
excellent saleswoman.'

Cassa felt herself flush. 'I wasn't aware of *selling* at
all,' she said stiffly. 'The customer came in to choose a
crystal and I helped her, that's all. She'd already made
up her mind to buy before she came into the shop. I
don't think I ever do any actual selling.'

He looked at her for a moment, then smiled slightly.
'No, perhaps you don't. And, in any case, I didn't
mean to be rude. Most shopkeepers are pleased to
think they're good salesmen.'

Cassa looked at him. He was standing with his head
tilted slightly to one side, a rather wry twist to his
mouth, but his lips were twitching as if he was about to
laugh. The feral look had left his eyes and he reminded
her of a small boy, begging for forgiveness. In spite of
herself, she felt an answering grin tug at her lips, and
she turned quickly away, tidying the display case and
closing it again.

'I'm sorry,' she said. 'You must think I'm very
touchy. Tell me about your book and why you think I
might be able to help you. Is it about Malvern?'

'In a way, yes,' he began, then broke off as three
more women came into the shop, talking excitedly
about the display of crystals and jewellery Cassa had
arranged in the small bow window. 'Look—I can't take
up any more of your time now. Can we meet later and
have a talk? Perhaps you'd come out to dinner with
James and me this evening?'

'That would be lovely,' Cassa said, wondering if she
meant that. Was 'lovely' a word that could ever be

applied to the company of this eagle-faced man? 'But, if you want to talk quietly, why don't you both come to supper with me? One of my customers gave me a huge piece of fresh salmon this morning—I've been hoping someone would come to share it. That's if you like salmon.'

'Who doesn't?' He put out his hand, smiling, and Cassa took it without thinking and immediately felt the tingling sensation that had made her jump earlier. She saw his eyes darken to pewter and caught her breath. What *was* it. . .?

'It's a deal, then,' Jet Tayler said after a brief pause. 'We'll come—when? Seven-thirty? And I'll bring the wine.' He moved to the door and stood shadowed against the light, while Cassa stood rubbing her hand with shaking fingers. 'We'll see you then.'

'Yes,' Cassa said faintly, watching him go, seeing him outlined for an instant against the bright sunlight. 'I'll see you then. . .'

The salmon was poached and cooling, and she was laying the table when the telephone rang. Cassa ran to answer it and heard James Meakin's voice on the line.

'Cassandra? Cassa, my dear, I'm so sorry but I find I can't come this evening. My sister's just rung—you know how it is.'

Cassa did indeed know how it was. James's elderly sister was subject to calling him frequently for 'emergencies' which rarely turned out to be real ones. But, just occasionally, they were, and James knew that, even if they weren't, her real need was for his company and attention and he never denied her those. 'If I don't go,' he would say with rueful humour, 'there really *will* be an emergency. And she was very good to me when our mother died, when I was only a boy.' He never seemed to question his sister's right to exact payment for that goodness, over half a century later.

'It's all right, James,' Cassa said, breaking into his apologies. 'Of course you must go. I'll send your salmon home in a doggie-bag.'

She heard James laugh. 'Well, that's the other thing, Cassa: Jet thinks you might prefer him not to come either, since you don't know him. Perhaps we ought to leave it for another evening.'

'Oh, really!' Cassa exclaimed. 'I don't need a chaperon, James. Of course he must still come.' She ignored the little voice inside her which suggested that it might be a very good idea indeed if Jet Tayler didn't come to spend the evening alone with her. 'Anyway, everything's ready now,' she said firmly. 'I'm not going to sit here and eat this salmon all by myself. Apart from which, I've got no wine to drink with it.'

James laughed again. He said something that Cassa couldn't hear, presumably to Jet. 'All right, then,' he said, coming back to the phone. 'He'll be with you as arranged. And if he doesn't behave himself you have my full permission to throw him out. With my doggie-bag, of course.'

'Of course,' Cassa agreed solemnly, and hung up. But her face was thoughtful as she went back to check on the table yet again. An evening alone with Jet Tayler was something she hadn't anticipated, and she wasn't at all sure she wanted it.

Just what was it about that man? He was attractive— exceptionally so. She'd already registered that slightly craggy face, those grey eyes that could flash with glittering silver, soften at a word or darken at a touch;

the slow, glinting smile, the thick bronze-gold hair that you wanted to run your fingers through. . . Cassa caught her breath. What on earth was she thinking of? So the man was good-looking—surely, at twenty-four, she wasn't susceptible to good looks without knowing the first thing about the man behind them? And, however attractive he might be, there was still that disquieting something, that sense of something untamed; still that tingling sensation when he touched her hand; the quivering inside when he looked into her eyes.

Did she want to experiment any more with any of those? Did she dare?

Well, it was done now. He was coming, and he was coming alone, and she must make the best of it. Serve him the meal she had perpared, answer whatever questions he wanted to ask, and then get rid of him. Quickly and without touching him.

That way, she'd be safe.

The doorbell rang almost before she was ready for it, and Cassa hurried to meet him at the top of the stairs, expecting him to be—like most of her visitors—puffing a little. Two flights of stairs, one up the outside of the house to the first floor, followed by another to her flat, tended to take people by surprise the first time. After that they just stopped for breath and to gather strength after the first flight. Women visitors usually wondered aloud how she managed with shopping.

Jet Tayler, however, was no more out of breath than if he had just strolled in from the next room.

'Well, this is pleasant,' he remarked as he stepped inside and glanced around the airy rooms. 'It doesn't looks so spacious from outside. And you've decorated it so well—all this pale silvery green gives it such a light, cool atmosphere.' He followed Cassa into the living-room and walked across to the window. 'And what a view! Straight out across the Severn Plain. That nearest hump must be Bredon Hill.'

'That's right. And the Cotswolds beyond.' Cassa came to stand beside him, keeping a careful twelve inches or so between them. The roofs of Malvern lay below them, giving way to the chequered fields and woods of Worcestershire. 'They say that if you stand on the Malvern Hills, looking east, the next high ground is the Russian Urals,' she told him. 'It seems incredible, doesn't it?'

'It certainly does.' He stood gazing out as Cassa fetched drinks. She came to stand beside him again and they sipped, looking out at the view that stretched before them. Cassa was acutely conscious of his nearness. She peeped sideways at him, wondering just how tall he was. Her dark close-cropped head barely reached his shoulder. He made her feel as small as an elf.

Jet turned his head suddenly and looked down at her, and Cassa quickly averted her eyes, feeling the colour warm her cheeks. She moved to one of the armchairs, deliberately avoiding the long, comfortable settee where she generally sat with her feet up. Jet stayed where he was, regarding her steadily and with a slight frown. Uneasily she wondered what was in his mind.

'Tell me about you boo——' she began.

'Tell me about yoursel——' The words came at the same moment. They both stopped and laughed a little.

'You first,' he said and then shook his head. 'No—me. You were going to ask about my book, and if I

begin on that I'll talk about nothing else. I'm a typical
male chauvinist, you see! And I want to know about
you.' He sat down in the armchair opposite, looking at
her very intently. 'Who are you, Cassa Newton? What
makes you tick? What are you about? I want to know.'

Cassa stared at him, feeling slightly breathless. It
was as if a searchlight had been turned on her, as if she
were about to be interrogated. She had never encoun-
tered such an intense interest before, and it was like
being suddenly caught up in a fierce gale. She found
herself gripping the arms of her chair, as if to stop
herself being swept away.

'That shop of yours,' he went on before she had a
chance to speak. 'How does it operate? Surely you
can't make a living out of bits of rock and the odd
scrap of jewellery? And all that spiel you were handing
that woman this afternoon—you don't really *believe* in
it, surely?'

Cassa felt a spasm of anger. She had met this attitude
many times before, of course, and could usually cope
with it, but tonight, coming from Jet Tayler, it was
more annoying than usual. Who was he, after all, to
accept an invitation to her home and then start to cast
doubt on her integrity?

'Of course I believe it,' she said coldly. 'I wouldn't
say it if I didn't. And I don't look on it as a "spiel".
I've already told you, I don't *sell* anything. People
either come in to buy or they don't. It's as simple as
that.'

'As the double-glazing salesman said,' he remarked,
and held up his hands as if to ward off a blow. 'All
right, it was a nasty crack—my sense of humour gets
the better of me at times. So convince me. Tell me
about crystals and what they can do—what you think

they can do. I imagine there must be some mystic purpose behind it all.'

Cassa gave him a suspicious look, but his face was perfectly grave and she decided to accept his half-apology. They had to talk about something, after all, while they spent this unexpected evening together. But she made up her mind not to wait too long before eating, and to bring the evening to a close as soon as possible afterwards. If only he would tell her what it was he wanted to know for his book!

'There's nothing new about crystals,' she said. 'They were used in Atlantis. And they knew far more about them then than we do—they used the energy from crystals to light their homes and power transport, as well as in healing of all kinds, as we're trying to learn to do now.'

Immediately, she knew that she had lost him. A look of incredulity appeared on his face and he drew back his head, turning it slightly as he stared at her. 'Fuel to light homes and power transport? From *crystals*? Cassa, you're an intelligent girl—you can't believe this!'

'Why not say instead that, as I'm an intelligent person and *do* believe it, it's worth more than an easy dismissal?' she retorted. 'You have only to look at history to see that there must be something in it—some truth that perhaps we haven't yet fully understood. And what's so strange about energy coming from crystals anyway? Why, they're used at the research establishment down the road for just that purpose, researching into semi-conductors. I don't understand all *that*—but I do know they can be used in all kinds of other ways. As they were by the Egyptians, and the Incas and the Aztecs—great civilisations.'

She stopped, aware that her voice was rising in her attempts to convince him, and picked up her glass. Jet was watching her closely, and she felt uncomfortable. 'You're looking at me as if I'm some kind of specimen,' she accused him at last.

Jet laughed. 'Not at all! I'm just fascinated by you. You're so—so eager, so enthusiastic. I really am sorry I implied you couldn't believe in it. You so clearly do.'

'But I'm not convincing you,' she said, and he grinned.

'It'll take a little longer than that, but I'd have a fairly open mind. In fact, I'd rather like to be convinced! It sounds such a magical world, where illnesses can be cured by a pretty stone—you did say they could be used for healing, didn't you? If they've been used for so long why do so few people know about them today? Why have we been bothering about doctors and hospitals all this time?'

He was still making fun of her, Cassa decided, but it was the usual reaction. It just meant that because he couldn't understand it, because it couldn't be explained in scientific terms, it couldn't be admitted. People were like that—particularly men. It was almost like the fear of the unknown.

'They were misused,' she said. 'Crystals have tremendous power and energy, and human beings always do misuse power in the end. Look what we're doing to the world today, from burning rainforests to covering the planet with waste products we don't know what to do with.' She caught the lift of his brows and felt a spurt of anger—did he really think she was nothing but a bimbo with no brains? Did he really believe she would never have thought about these things? 'Well, the power of crystals was misused too;

their energies became unstable and eventually caused the eruptions which lost Atlantis forever. That's how powerful they are.'

'Power indeed,' he commented. 'And now? Have their powers been mysteriously renewed?'

'It seems so,' Cassa said, focusing her mind on the positive aspects of this conversation. People had been convinced before, even people as sceptical as Jet Tayler. 'All over the world, people are finding that the powers can be used again—but only and always for the good of mankind. We must never make the mistake of exploiting them again.' She paused. Was she talking too much? But she believed so strongly in what she said, and if there was a chance of convincing him. . .

'And you believe that selling them in a shop is going to do good to mankind?' he asked disbelievingly.

'Why not? That woman this afternoon might not have looked like a world saviour, but who knows what she will become once she gets to know her crystal? And even if she only does a tiny bit of good—and everyone else who buys and uses a crystal does a tiny bit of good—well, isn't that better?'

'All right, I get the message.' He waved a hand. 'And clearly you believe in it, so I won't argue. But I'm afraid all this mysticism passes me by. I like to know how things *work*—what makes them go. Including people. I might be fascinated by *you*, Cassa, but I'll never be fascinated by your crystals.'

'That's all right,' she said equably. 'I'm not trying to sell you one.'

Jet laughed suddenly. '*Touché*!' He looked around the room and got up to look at the display of stones Cassa had on a sidetable. 'They're certainly very attractive, anyway. Tell me what they are.'

'No, it's time to eat now.' Cassa made up her mind to keep control of this evening in her own hands. She led him into the small dining-room, still with the same view of the Severn Plain, and sat him at the little round table while she went out to fetch the starters. 'Now,' she said, returning with pears filled with Stilton and walnuts, 'it's your turn. Tell me how you come to be in Malvern, writing a book.'

Jet grinned, and again Cassa realised what a very attractive smile he had. Quite devastating, in fact, the way his mouth widened and his eyes crinkled. . . Stop it! she admonished herself severely. He's not your type. Nothing *like* your type. In fact. . .he spells danger.

The thought gave a her a little shiver, a shiver which ran lightly across her skin like fingers that barely touched. . . With an almost visible effort she brought her attention back to what Jet was saying.

'I've been a bit of a dilettante, I'm afraid,' he told her cheerfully. 'Set out to be an academic, but the cloistered life didn't suit me at all—I like to be free. Lecturing was all right, I got on well with my students, but there are so many restrictions—you can't *explore*. Not as much as I wanted to anyway. And my music took up too much time——'

'Your music?' Cassa was interested in spite of herself. 'Do you play?'

'Oh, yes,' he said casually. 'Cello mostly, but I'd fond of the violin as well, and, of course, I had to learn the piano. And I like to compose too. But you can't do all that and lecture too, *and* write the kind of learned theses and papers that academics have to do. I felt as if I were being buried in it all. Had to get away.' He helped himself to some more dressing. 'These pears are really very good. Just right for a hot summer evening.'

'I'm glad you like them. But if you enjoyed music so much why didn't you take it up as a career? Play in an orchestra? Or are you good enough to play solo?'

'I could have been,' he said thoughtfully, 'if I'd concentrated on it. But——' his shoulders moved '—it was like everything else. Too much of a tie. I told you—I'm a butterfly.'

'People say I am too,' Cassa said, gathering the plates together. 'Perhaps we're the same star sign.'

'The same——? Oh, I see. Astrology!' Jet's grin was half amused, half patronising. 'I suppose I might have known you'd be into astrology too. Well, what sign are you?'

'Gemini.' Cassa went out to the tiny kitchen and brought in the plate of salmon, garnished with cucumber, that had been intended to serve three. A bowl of salad stood ready on the side-table, and new potatoes were keeping hot in a bowl. She served the salmon on to plates, leaving Jet to help himself to vegetables, and he poured the wine he had brought.

'Very civilised,' he said. 'The ideal way to spend an evening. . . So you're Gemini. What's that—twins or something, isn't it?'

'You do know a little about it, then?'

'One can hardly help hearing something about it,' he said dismissively. 'It doesn't mean I know anything about it.'

'Or want to,' Cassa said. 'All right, so you're not a Gemini—what are you? Let me try to guess.'

She rested her chin on her hand and gazed at him across the table, her dark green eyes like crystals themselves as they examined him. For a moment or

two she was totally absorbed, assessing all that she had
sensed and noticed about this man, trying to find the
astrological sign that would fit him best.

'You just could be a Capricorn,' she decided at last.
'Pedantic, meticulous, needing to have everything
proved to you. Absolutely convinced of your own
opinions. Perhaps you're not a butterfly at all—you're
just so sure you're good at everything that you want
everyone else to see it too. But, underneath, you're
ambitious, and once you decide just which ambition to
go for you'll chuck all the others and think of nothing
else. And you—— What's the matter? What have I
said?'

Jet threw back his head and laughed.

'Nothing. Everything. You talk about *me* being so
sure I'm right! And there you sit, burbling away about
astrology and what star sign I must be as if you had
some divine knowledge. Capricorn! Pedantic, meticulous, down to earth. . .!' He roared with laughter again
while Cassa sat staring at him, feeling her face grow
hotter and her heart thump with embarrassment and
annoyance. 'Cassa, you're marvellous, absolutely
marvellous.'

'I'm glad you think so,' she said icily. 'So what sign
are you, then? Or perhaps you don't even know.'

'Well, I know I'm not Capricorn,' he pointed out,
and his eyes gleamed with a teasing light. 'Now, shall I
tell you or shall I make you go through the whole lot
until you strike lucky? No, that wouldn't be much
thanks for the delicious meal you've taken so much
trouble to prepare.' He grinned that wide, engaging
smile that had already begun to twist her heart in
knots. 'I'll put you out of your misery. I was born in

February—the third, to be exact. So that makes
me——'

'Aquarius!' Cassa stared at him. 'But—are you *sure*?
I mean——' as he began to laugh again '—of course I
know you're sure about when you were born. But
you're not *like* an Aquarius!'

'Which just goes to show how ridiculous it all is,' he
said triumphantly. 'Does everyone born on the same
day as I was have to be exactly alike? Of course not!
So——'

'Well, of course everyone is an individual,' Cassa
admitted. 'But Aquarius people are generally more
ready to be interested; they're not so dismissive—those
are definitely Capricorn characteristics. Still people do
sometimes display other characteristics. Maybe you're
not very comfortable with yourself at present—you've
told me you've found it difficult to settle. Maybe you
need to be more like a Capricorn just now.'

Jet stared at her. His eyes darkened a little and he
moved in his chair. Cassa felt a tiny thrill run though
her. Had she struck a nerve? But almost before she
had formed the thought he had given a short laugh and
was speaking again, and the uneasiness she thought she
detected in the first few words was gone almost before
she could be sure of it.

'If that isn't just like a star-gazer!' he jeered. 'Prove
you wrong and straight away you come up with some
twist in the tale to prove yourself right. As for being
interested in things—I am. I'm interested in you, for a
start. I want to know more about you and these crystals
of yours—what you believe they can do, what you
think you can do with them. I want to know what it
means, what it means to *you*. I want to know what
makes you tick, what makes you get out of bed in the

mornings.' He leaned forward, eyes like silver as he let his voice grow more intent, emphasising his words. 'I want to *know*, Cassa—but that doesn't mean to say I'll believe, not just like that. I'll want to think about what you tell me, analyse it, turn it over in my mind. And then I'll decide for myself.'

Cassa stared at him. A *frisson* touched her skin, and she felt her heart quiver.

'Yes,' she said slowly. 'Yes, you *are* an Aquarius man. A man of the Age of Aquarius, searching for the truth, searching for rainbows at midnight. And you'll find them, too, and take them to pieces to see what they're made of and how they work. But will you ever be able to put them together again? Or will there always be a piece left over?'

'A small bit of indigo, perhaps,' he said, only just above his breath. 'Just a scrap of violet silk, fluttering in the breeze. But by then I'll have gone on to another rainbow. You see, Cassa, I *am* a butterfly. Or perhaps a grasshopper would be a better metaphor. I never settle anywhere for very long before I want to leap away.'

He's warning me, Cassa thought. He's telling me not to let myself get interested in him. He'd like to be friends, but he won't commit himself. Yes. . .he *is* an Aquarius man. . .

She stood up abruptly, breaking the spell that had begun to weave itself like a fine web around them, and took the plates, surprised to find that hers was empty. She must have eaten, although she had no recollection of it. There was home-made lemon sorbet to follow, served in pretty glass dishes. She switched on the coffee-maker and returned to the table, still thoughtfully silent.

'You were telling me about yourself,' she reminded him. 'About your music and why you didn't go on with lecturing. So what did you do?'

Jet shrugged. 'Anything and everything. Travelled, keeping myself with articles for the Sunday supplements. Wrote a book or two, mostly about travel in far-flung places like the Andes or Patagonia. Did you know there's a thriving Welsh community in Patagonia? Then I drifted into doing a couple of biographies of musicians, which went down quite well. And my publishers asked me to do some more.'

'Biographies? But isn't that just what you hate—being tied down? I can't think of anything more restrictive than having to concentrate on one person's life, unable to let your own personality through. And the research—surely it's just the kind of thing that would drive you mad if you're as restless as you say you are?'

'Oh, I don't mind being tied down so long as I'm doing the tying,' he said. 'It's being tied down by other people I can't stand. And I let my personality through, as you call it, by concentrating on those parts of the subject's own personality that are most interesting to me.'

'Like all biographers, in fact,' Cassa said. 'Distorting the truth.' And gasped a little. She hadn't meant to say that at all, even though it was what she thought.

Jet opened his eyes wide. 'That sounded as if I'd struck a nerve.'

'I'm sorry,' she said, recovering. 'I didn't mean to be rude. But don't you think it's inevitable? None of us can fully understand another person, especially when he or she has been dead for a long time. Or even a short time. So how can anyone write a really truthful account of that person? How can you even try to present the character as he or she really was?'

'Does any biographer claim to do that? All we do is tell it as it seems to us——'

'And not even care if you hurt other people in the process,' she broke in. 'Don't you see, there are always people who can be hurt, unless your subject is so far back in history that it doesn't matter any more? But you don't care about that. Your only concern is about telling the story the way *you* see it. And about making money from it,' she added bitterly.

Jet stared at her.

'Cassa——'

'Oh, let it rest,' she said impatiently. 'I'm sorry; I shouldn't let it get to me. Please—tell me about your book. I assume it's another biography. And, if it's about Malvern and it's a musician, it must be. . .' Her voice faded and she stared at him. Her skin grew cold, then warm again, and she stood up abruptly, dropping her napkin on the table.

Jet stood up too. He towered above her, making her feel smaller than ever. For a moment she felt a tremor of fear.

'Elgar,' she said flatly. 'Sir Edward Elgar. The letters. That's why you're here, isn't it? That's why James brought you to see me?'

Jet nodded slowly. 'That's why.' He reached out almost diffidently and touched her arm. 'Cassa——'

But Cassa leapt away as if she had been stung. To have him touching her, after all she had discovered about him. . .to feel that sharp tingle as his fingertips brushed her skin. . .to feel her heart kick and her stomach twist. . . No, it was too much. She shook her head violently and crossed her arms over her body as if to protect herself.

'No,' she whispered. 'No. . .'

'Cassa, they're not *your* letters. They belong to everyone, everyone who's interested in the greatest English composer who ever lived. They're part of our heritage——'

'No.'

'Cassa, they could solve the mystery of the thirteenth *Variation*, the *Enigma* itself. They could tell us just who is represented by that piece of music. Not Lady Mary Lygon, as people thought for so long, nor Helen Weaver, his early fiancée, but someone else, someone totally unknown, someone Elgar loved and remembered and——'

'And wanted to protect!' Cassa exclaimed. 'Don't you see, he *wanted* her to remain a mystery, he wanted her to be hidden? He didn't name her because he didn't *want* to. And, whether the secret's in those letters or not, I'm not going to help you solve the mystery now— not even if everyone *is* dead.' She flung up her head and met his eyes squarely, her own glittering like emeralds in her luminous face. 'Yes, you *are* an Aquarius man! You want to know everything, you want to take it all to pieces and look at it and see what makes it work. Never mind that other people don't want to be analysed, to have their secrets revealed— that doesn't matter to you. You've just got to *know*. And you can't even let it stop there—you've got to tell everyone else too. Well, this is one secret you won't pull to pieces, Jet Tayler—not as long as I hold the key, if key there is. This is one thing you *aren't* going to find out.'

She held his look for a long moment, then turned

away. Jet stood quite still in the middle of the room as
she walked to the window and stared out, her arms still
wrapped around her body, breathing hard. Dusk was
settling on the plain, and the lights of Malvern and the
villages were beginning to twinkle. She bit her lip,
feeling suddenly tearful, almost as if she had just lost
something precious.

Jet moved and spoke, his voice low in the twilit
room.

'I'm sorry, Cassa. I didn't mean to upset you. And
I'd dearly like to know why you are so against my
seeing these letters—why you're so against biographers
at all. But I don't think this is the moment to discuss
it—or anything else.' He waited a moment or two, but
Cassa did not move. She heard him move away. When
he spoke next, it was from the doorway.

'I think I'd better go now, Cassa. Thank you for a
truly delicious meal. And I hope you'll agree to see me
again. I think we ought to discuss this further, when
you're feeling less upset.'

'There's nothing to discuss,' she said quietly.

'Well, perhaps not. But there's no reason why we
can't be friends.' He waited a moment. 'Goodnight,
Cassa.'

She whispered something, hardly knowing what it
was, knowing only that her heart was crying out,
begging him not to go. But what use was that? He'd
told her clearly enough what kind of man he was. He'd
told her plainly that he was an Aquarian, wanting only
friendship, shying away from commitment. And they
would never agree on the way he earned his living.

The door closed softly and she knew he had gone.
For a long time she stood at the window, gazing out
over the plain until it was fully dark, a velvet blackness

pierced by the lights of distant houses. Then she turned and looked at the table where they had sat together and talked and argued.

I haven't fallen in love, she told herself fiercely. I haven't fallen in love. I *haven't*.

CHAPTER TWO

EVEN when she had finished clearing away the remains of dinner, Cassa was still too restless and disturbed to go to bed. Instead, she went into the sitting-room and sank into the big armchair by the window, staring out at the fading view.

Her mind was filled with Jet Tayler and the letters he so badly wanted to see. They had come to light only recently, found in a box in the attic of the house where she had her flat—the house that had been in her family ever since it was built some time in the nineteeth century. Cassa's father had converted it into flats when it had been clear it was too big for him and his wife, and Cassa had been delighted to be given her own, here on the second floor, where she had this wonderful view. Her parents had kept the first floor for themselves, and the top flat, tiny but charming with its attic rooms and sloping ceilings, was currently empty.

The letters had been among a mass of accumulated debris, which had been brought down to the basement and left to be sorted later. And it had been only just before their trip to Australia to visit Cassa's brother that Dr Newton had discovered them.

'It seems to be a correspondence between Elgar and a young woman who lived in this house some time in the 1890s,' he told them at dinner that night. Cassa had come down to share a last meal with her parents, and James Meakin was with them too. 'We always knew this was one of the houses he visited, of course—he

used to play music with my great-uncle, who owned
the house at that time. But there were no daughters of
the family, so just who the girl was isn't clear. And I
haven't had the time to look at the letters properly, but
at a quick glance they do seem to be quite affectionate.'

'Another love?' James Meakin suggested, his eyes
gleaming behind his spectacles. 'He was a personable
young man—there must have been quite a few hearts
fluttering around this area. Or perhaps the affection
was only on her side.'

'Well, I haven't time to read them before we go
away.' John Newton sounded regretful. 'I'm almost
tempted to take them with me—but that would be
foolish. They could so easily get lost of destroyed on
such a long journey. I daren't risk that. No, they'll
have to wait till we come back.'

'And, no doubt, as the discoverer of such an important correspondence, you'll want to be the first to read
them,' James observed wistfully, and his old friend
laughed.

'Well, wouldn't you? They've lain in our attic for
long enough—they can wait a few more months. But
I'll leave them in Cassa's safe keeping—and hope she'll
have the will power to resist having a peep!'

Cassa had smiled, but she knew that, although her
father had spoken jokingly, he really did hope to be
the first to read the letters Sir Edward Elgar, genius of
English music, had written to a girl who had lived in
this very house. Her own heart had beaten faster at the
thought—and now, sitting at her window and thinking
of that girl, who had grown old and died since those
letters were written, she felt that quickening heartbeat
again. And it kicked even more wildly when the image
of Jet Tayler came into her mind.

Why had James told him about the letters? Oh, she supposed it was understandable enough. James had clearly been intrigued by the discovery and longing to see them himself—James was possessed of an insatiable curiosity, and Elgar was one of his great heroes. And, knowing that Jet was embarking on a new biography, he hadn't been able to resist the urge to tell him. And Jet, naturally, would want to see the letters too—even though nobody yet knew what was in them. They could be nothing more than a casual correspondence.

Or they could, as Jet had suggested, be the answer to the great question Edward Elgar had left behind him—the unanswered question of the *Enigma Variations*, that great work of his that had portrayed so many of his friends in music and yet left just one—the thirteenth—to be a mystery to tease his followers. Who *did* he have in mind when he wrote that lovely, romantic melody? Was it, as had so often been suggested, Lady Mary Lygon? Or his one-time financée Helen Weaver?

Or was it someone else—someone whose memory had been hidden, but someone Elgar himself had never forgotten and chosen to remember in this last, secret way?

'They could solve the mystery of the thirteenth Variation,' Jet had said passionately. But suppose Elgar hadn't wanted it solved? Didn't he have a right to his mystery? What right had Jet Tayler or anyone else to unravel it and tell the world?

And the girl herself—she might have sat here, at this very window, watching for him to come and fill the house with the sound of his violin. She might have sat listening to that sound, dreaming her dreams. She might have waved goodbye to him from this window as he strode away along Abbey Road, towards the old gateway.

Didn't she too, even though she had died long ago, have her own right to her secret, her dreams?

No, Cassa thought with sudden violence, I shan't let him see the letters. I shan't let anyone see them—I shan't even look at them myself, tempted though I might be, just in case he can see into my mind with those silver-grey eyes of his, and read the secrets there. He must write his biography without them.

Slowly, stiffly, she uncurled herself and stood up. Her mind was unsettled, her heart jerking, her emotions in turmoil. She needed calm and tranquillity before she would be able to sleep.

She went to her glass-topped cabinet, where all her crystals were displayed on their velvet bed, and chose an amethyst. The deep glowing colour was already bringing peace to her heart as she took it in her hand, and the feel of its jagged yet perfectly regular contours seemed to draw away the uncertainty and conflict of the past few hours. She held it, warming it in her palm, and then took it back to the chair by the window.

Nobody could get at her now, she thought, willing herself to accept the stone's healing influence. Not even Jet Tayler, with his glinting grey eyes and his devastating smile. Nobody could disturb the peace that she could draw on, deep within her.

Her mind was calm again, the tumult stilled, when she finally went to bed.

'Why did you do it?'

The peace, so hard-won the night before, left Cassa's heart as she faced her father's old friend the next day.

The crystal shop was empty and she had been rearranging the display cabinet when he'd come in to apologise for not being able to come for dinner with Jet. She stood with a silver ankh hung on a heavy chain, in her hand, and accused him with green eyes. 'Why did you tell him about the letters?'

James Meakin lifted his hands. 'Why not? He's a biographer, I know him well, I count him as a friend—how could I not have told him about this new discovery? It was the natural thing to do.'

Cassa sighed. 'But Dad's your friend too. And we haven't told anyone else about the letters—they're our own private business.'

'Then they shouldn't be. Cassa, Elgar is a public figure, of public interest. *Anything* relevant to his life should be in the public domain. Don't you see——'

'No, I don't!' Angry and upset, Cassa let the ankh drop into the case, and spread its chain out with shaking fingers. 'I'm sorry, James, it isn't any use; if you're here to plead Jet Tayler's case you're wasting your time. I shall never let him see the letters. He can forget they even exist. He can forget *I* exist—I certainly intend to forget I ever met *him*!'

'Well, there's a declaration,' a deep voice drawled from the doorway. 'What a strong-minded young woman it is, indeed. And what a pity she won't be able to carry out her intentions!'

Cassa whirled and gasped as the tall figure of Jet Tayler shadowed the doorway. Without realising how it had got there, she found her hand at her throat, almost in protection. She took a step backwards, feeling her heart leap in her breast, and reached out one hand for something solid.

Jet came into the shop. The only light was from his

eyes, a strange, silvery gleam that seemed to reflect in the crystals that lay exposed to his gaze. He glanced at them with dismissal before his eyes came back to Cassa, moving slowly over her as if assessing the slender body beneath the silky multi-coloured dress that skimmed her figure.

James Meakin murmured something about his sister and melted away. Cassa put out her other hand in a feeble attempt to keep him, but he was gone, sliding past Jet, who acknowledged him with a movement of his hand before moving nearer to Cassa. She found herself backed against the display case, staring up at him with wide, cat-like green eyes, her trembling lips parting as she tried to whisper words that refused to come.

'You look disturbed, Cassa,' he said in a low voice. 'What is it? What's upsetting you?'

You know very well what's disturbing me, she thought furiously. You're doing it deliberately— coming in here when you *know* I never want to see you again, when you know the effect you have on me. You knew it last night and you know it now. And I'm *not* falling in love with you—I don't even *like* you. So just—just go away and *stop it*!

But, badly though she wanted to say the words, they would not come to her lips, and she shook her head, eyes begging him to keep his distance. She had little hope of his doing so, however. And her fears were realised as he lifted one long-fingered hand and touched her cheek with the tips of his fingers. They burned like fire on her sensitive skin.

'Don't look so frightened, little one,' he murmured, letting his fingers trail slowly down her cheek, tracing the line of her neck to rest lightly in the hollow of her collarbone. 'Nothing's going to happen to you—nothing you don't want to happen, that is.'

Cassa jerked her head away, angered by the sudden heat that flooded her body, knowing that it must be betrayed in the warm colour she felt in her face. 'And just what do you mean by that? Why are you here, anyway? I'm sure you're not interested in crystals.'

'Oh, I don't know,' he drawled. 'I can be interested in most things. Believing in them is a different matter, of course. But you're right—I didn't come in to inspect your wares. At least. . .' his eyes moved over her face and then down her body before he glanced into her eyes again with a wicked twinkle '. . .not the ones you have for sale, anyway!'

Cassa gasped and twisted away from him, outraged, although she knew that she would have done no more than laugh if another man had talked to her in that way. But then it would have been no more than a light, somewhat daring flirtation—whereas with Jet Tayler it meant something different.

Yet just what *was* the difference? What did it mean when this man touched her with his fingertips and let his eyes drift over her body? What was the silvery glance saying to her heart? What was going on in his mind?

'So just why are you here?' She felt her skin shiver away from contact with his. 'I thought we said all there was to say last night.'

'Did you? Personally, I thought we'd scarcely begun.' To her infinite relief, he moved away from her and leaned back against a cabinet of silver jewellery, which Cassa had bought from a local craftsman. 'I had the impression that we two had a *lot* to say to one another. Don't you have that feeling too?'

'No, I don't,' she snapped and took advantage of her opportunity to step behind the desk where the till stood. Most customers accepted the implication that this was forbidden territory—but would Jet, the untamed, the feral, consider that any territory was forbidden to him? She had a feeling that Jet was never, in any circumstances, to be thought of in the same light as 'most customers'.

'I don't think I have anything at all to say to you,' she said defiantly. 'The letters are private. You can't see them, and that's all there is to it. In any case, they belong to my father and he's in Australia.'

'Yes, so I understand. Well, Australia's not so very far away. I believe letters can be pretty well relied on to get through these days, and there's this new-fangled invention called the telephone. I dare say your father would be willing to talk, even if you're not.'

'You don't know his——' Cassa began, and then stopped. Jet didn't know Brian's address or phone number—but James Meakin would. And James had already shown himself to be on Jet's side over this. She wouldn't put it past him to ring her father himself and persuade him that Cassa must be told to give up the letters.

Well, she wouldn't, she told herself dramatically—she'd die first. Elgar and his young correspondent had a right to their privacy. She wasn't going to help any self-interested biographer—no, forget that word, *Nosy-Parker* to pry into their secrets. If secrets there were.

She had a brief wistful thought that it was a pity she'd promised her father that she wouldn't look at the letters herself. After all, she couldn't help being curious. . .but almost at once she admonished herself.

You're as bad as he is, she thought, looking across the counter at Jet Tayler. You're as inquisitive as everyone else.

She found herself meeting Jet's eyes, and felt her skin warm with yet another blush. He was watching her steadily, his eyes noting every change of expression on her face, as if he could read exactly what was going on in her mind. She remembered the uncomfortable feeling she'd had last night that he could do just that, and turned quickly away, fiddling with a pile of letters that had lain unattended on the counter since she had come in.

'I'm sorry,' she said, speaking quickly, breathlessly, 'you'll have to go now. I really am very busy. As you can see——' she waved her hand vaguely around the empty shop '——I do have a lot to do,' she insisted rather feebly.

'Oh, I can see that,' Jet agreed gravely. 'And I'd be the last to hold you up.' His tone was perfectly serious, but the twitch of muscles around his mouth betrayed an infuriating desire to burst out laughing. 'Tell you what,' he went on, leaning companionably against the counter, 'suppose I leave you alone now to get on with your work——' he glanced around the quiet little shop '——and in return you come out with me this evening, so that I can repay your hospitality? I'd really like that.'

Cassa stared at him. This man really was persistent. His tenacity was more like that of a Capricorn. And he actually thought he could win—wear her down—so that in the end, if only for the sake of a quiet life, she'd do what he asked and hand over the letters. Well, he had another think coming!

'Look,' she said through her teeth, 'I don't have to make any bargains with you to get a bit more space in my shop. You can stay as long as you like—you won't disturb me.' And that was one of the biggest lies she'd ever told, she thought wryly. 'Nor will you persuade me to come out with you,' she went on, picking up one of the letters at random and inserting the paper-knife into the envelope. 'I've already said that I think we've done all the talking we need to do. Now, if you'll excuse me. . .'

'Certainly,' he agreed, and went on leaning against the counter, watching her with bright eyes. 'My, you really do lead a hectic life, don't you? There must be all of half a dozen letters there. Two of them junk mail, if I'm any judge.' He gazed at the highly coloured envelope Cassa was slitting open now. 'What's that—a book club, photo processing, some marvellous prize you've already won and only have to claim? Whatever it is, you seem to be finding it a lot more interesting than I ever find my junk mail!'

Cassa threw down the leaflet she'd been staring at without even knowing what it was. 'I'm surprised you've ever settled in one place long enough to receive junk mail! Look, Mr Tayler——'

'Jet. We'd progressed as far as Christian names last night—don't you remember?'

'—why don't you go away and find someone else to pester? Don't you have any research to do? Elgar did have other connections around here, you know—he lived in twenty-five different houses, for a start. Can't you go and search their attics for forgotten love-letters?'

'What a marvellous idea,' he drawled. 'I might even do just that. After you've agreed to come out for dinner with me.'

Exasperated, Cassa stared at him. His grey eyes,

bright as early-evening stars, gazed back unwinkingly. She saw his mouth twitch and, infuriated though she was, felt her own lips tremble in response. Quickly, she turned her head away but Jet reached one hand across the counter and caught her chin, forcing her to face him. And, to her infinite annoyance, she felt a smile begin to curve her lips.

'There!' he exclaimed triumphantly. 'I knew there was a human being lurking in there somewhere. Come on, Cassa, why not say yes? I promise not to even mention Elgar or his letters—you can talk about crystals or astrology or the price of fish if you like. But I'd really like you to come out with me.'

Cassa struggled mentally for just one more minute before giving in. Then she let her smile grow, reluctantly, and laughed.

'Oh, all right. I'll come.' And then, thinking that her acceptance sounded less than gracious, she added, 'I'd like to. But I'll hold you to that promise.'

'Hold me to anything—I'll enjoy it,' he said wickedly, and Cassa felt her blush surge yet again. How long was it, for goodness' sake, since she'd felt her colour rise so often? That was something she'd thought had been left behind with her teens. 'I'll pick you up at seven, if that's all right,' he went on, levering himself upright away from the counter. 'And, having extracted that promise from you, I really will leave you to get on with your work. You're right—I do have research to do.' He gave her a cheerful wave and strode out of the shop, pausing as he went past the window to wave again.

Cassa watched him go, fighting a feeling of helplessness. What *was* it about this man? He seemed to be able to twist her round his little finger—and no man had done that to her since—well, not for a long, long time, anyway. She didn't know whether she liked him or not, though she had to admit that until she'd found out about his interest in the Elgar letters she had found him attractive. But, even then, there'd been something more than mere attraction or liking—some undercurrent of stronger emotion, a ripple of unease somewhere in her heart, as if that very attraction could be perilous to her. And she recalled her words to herself last night, repeated over and over again in her mind almost as if they were a mantra, a good-luck charm to ward off danger: I am *not* falling in love.

Falling in love? With Jet Tayler? No way!

The sun had disappeared behind the bulk of the Malvern Hills as Cassa got ready to go out that evening with Jet Tayler. She stood in her bedroom at the back of the house, staring out at the trees that massed up the hill as she tried to decide what to wear.

It didn't help that she had no idea where they might be going. There were so many good eating-places in the area. Would he be taking her out for a really nice pub meal, such as she had enjoyed at the Pheasant in Welland. . .a bistro meal in Upton upon Severn. . .a dinner at one of the locals hotels, like the Feathers in Ledbury. . .a Chinese, an Indian, or even a French meal at that very exclusive restaurant at Malvern Wells?

She finally settled on a new skirt in dramatic dark red with a pattern of swirling gold, with which she wore a plain gold T-shirt top in thin silk. Her favourite crystal hung round her neck on a slender silver chain, and she fitted tiny crystal earrings into her ears before brushing back her almost black hair into its smooth cap. Green eyes glittered back at her from the mirror as she flicked mascara over her lashes, and she slicked on a film of gold-dusted lipstick and decided that was enough. It wouldn't do for Jet to think she was making a special effort for him!

The doorbell rang as she was spraying a fine aura of sandalwood perfume in a mist around her, and she waited a moment or two before going slowly to answer it.

'Oh, hello.' She hoped her casual tone successfully concealed the rapid beating of her heart. 'I'm just ready. Do you want to come in for a drink first?'

'No, we'll go straight off.' His eyes moved over her, speaking his appreciation of her looks. 'Very nice indeed. What I don't quite understand is how come an attractive girl like you has time to go out with me at such short notice?'

'Oh, I like to keep the odd evening free,' she said airily, slipping through the door and locking it behind her. 'You never know what might turn up. And I do actually enjoy *not* going out every night. I'm one of those strange people who enjoy their own company.'

'Not strange at all, when the company's so good,' he responded gallantly, and Cassa laughed and made up her mind that they were going to have fun this evening. So long as he kept off the subject of Elgar. . .

Jet Tayler's car was waiting in the drive—a low, sleek BMW with a colour that matched his eyes. There's stylish! she thought with a quiver of amusement that didn't quite hide the impressed feeling the car gave her. He pretended to be a bit of a dilettante, with his casual references to travelling where the mood took him, supporting himself by the odd Sunday-supplement article, but you didn't pay for cars like this by being a butterfly.

Or maybe he had other money—family money. Maybe he really was not much more than a playboy, taking up this or that for fun and a bit of pocket-money. Just how serious was he about this biography, for instance?

Well, she could hardly introduce the subject, having forbidden it for the entire evening. She slipped into the passenger-seat, smiling her thanks as he closed the door carefully for her, and looked with interest around the interior as he went round to the driver's seat and got in.

But it was difficult to keep away from the reason why he was in Malvern. Her polite question as to how long he intended to stay took him—naturally enough— to the reply, 'However long it takes to do the research I came for.' And there they were, on forbidden ground once more.

Hastily, she cast around for another topic, and came up with, 'Where's your home? I mean, where were you brought up?'

'That's two questions,' he said, driving the car fast along the road that led away from Malvern and into Herefordshire. 'I was born in Suffolk but I only lived there for a few weeks. My parents were musicians, you see, and travelled all over the world. They didn't believe in leaving baby behind, so I went along too. I was brought up everywhere.'

'That must have been a tremendous experience. Where do they live now?'

'In Florida. I don't get to see them very often. Dad had a weak chest and years of touring didn't do him much good, and Mother wouldn't go without him, so they retired. They live a delightfully lazy life now, pottering about, doing a bit of sailing, a bit of fishing, taking off for a trip to the Bahamas when the mood takes them.'

'Sounds wonderful.'

'Oh, it is. Right up my street, in fact. I often threaten to move in with them but they won't have it—they're like swans; threw their cygnet out of the nest and won't let him back in on any account.'

Cassa glanced sideways at him, noting the profile that was saved from a disconcerting perfection by a certain cragginess of the jawline. A strong face, she thought, and one that belied his claims to laziness. And she'd already realised that inside that high, broad forehead there was a very lively mind—one that wasn't to be trifled with.

'Haven't you ever wanted to settle down?' she asked curiously. 'Have a steady career, a home? Or do you have one somewhere?'

'What do you think? That I'm some kind of gipsy?' His grey eyes laughed at her and she felt hot and uncomfortable. 'Of course I have a home, Cassa. I have a very pleasant cottage—though it's a bit large to be called that; in fact, it's a converted barn—in Cornwall. It's as near as I can get to Florida! But I don't get there very often—I suppose I've travelled too much to ever want to settle in one place for long.'

'And your career?' She was aware of approaching forbidden ground again. 'Don't you have any ambition?'

Jet took a few moments before answering her. They had passed through the little town of Ledbury with its black and white buildings and ancient market place, and plunged into the mass of side-roads and lanes that wove about off the Ross-on-Wye road. At last, slowing down for a narrow bend, he said quietly, 'Yes, I have ambitions. All I need is enough lifetimes to achieve them all.' He stopped suddenly in a field gateway and turned in his seat to look searingly into her eyes. Cassa shrank back in her seat, wondering in sudden panic what he meant to do, but he did not touch her. He didn't have to. His look was enough to burn into her skin.

'Don't you ever feel that, Cassa?' he asked, his voice intense. 'That there just isn't time in one life to do all there is to be done? Life—it's such an *experience*. And there's so much of it out there, waiting to be sampled. How can anyone settle down in a little three-bedroomed semi and call that living? How can anyone tie themselves down to one life, one place—one person—when they haven't even begun to look at what's out there?' He waved a hand at the fields and woods that rolled away from them. 'Cassa, I've been travelling since I was six weeks old and I've only just begun to see what there is to be seen. I haven't done one tenth—no, not one thousandth of all the things I want to do. I know I never will—but I'll tell you this; I'll have a damned good try!'

Cassa stared at him. His intensity was almost frightening but she couldn't let it go unchallenged. She shook her head slowly.

'You've got it wrong, Jet. You don't have to go travelling the world looking for life. It's everywhere. It's in the three-bedroomed semi just as much as in Florida, or China, or the Antarctic. Life is *people*, not places, not even experiences. Life's inside you, not outside, not on the other side of the world.' She shook her head again. 'I'm sorry for you, Jet. You're going to waste the life you think you value so much, searching for something that's probably under your nose the whole time.'

They sat silently for a few moments, their eyes locked. Then he sighed and ran his long, tapering musician's fingers through his thick, burnished hair.

'I wish I could believe you, Cassa. I almost wish I could believe you. But I'm afraid I know better. I've seen more than you, tucked away in your cosy little country town, running your fancy shop. You know, you could do better than that. You're a bright girl; you could go a long way.'

'Thanks,' she said, annoyed, 'but I don't happen to want to go a long way. You see, I'm not like you—I'm happy where I am.'

Jet started the car again. 'I know,' he said softly as it purred like a great cat under his stroking hands, 'and that's what I find so intriguing about you.'

They drove on in silence, Cassa fighting her irritation. He was so convinced he was right! And she was equally convinced he was wrong. How could she make him see the truth?

Why should she even want to?

To her surprise, they drew up a few minutes later at a small black- and white-timbered inn that she had never seen before. She stared at it, at the rose-strewn garden that surrounded it, the little stream that trickled through its tiny yard. It was almost as if it had sprung up there by magic. How was it she had never known about it and yet Jet had driven here as if he had known it all his life?

'I reserved a table,' he remarked and took her elbow to steer her through the small bar to a minute restaurant with only half a dozen tables, overlooking the garden and the tumbling hills beyond. Their table was ready for them, by the window, but at the landlady's suggestion they took their drinks out to the little garden and studied the menu under the blossom-laden branches of an old apple tree.

'A good selection,' Jet remarked after a few moments. 'Anything you fancy, Cassa?'

'Just about all of it,' she said with feeling. 'I shall never choose! Devilled whitebait sounds marvellous, but so do the stuffed peaches and the parma ham and melon. And that's only the starters! And then we've got to think about whether to have roast guinea-fowl, or Wye salmon, or chicken with cashews, or pork with cider, or—no, it's just impossible. How did you find out about this place, Jet? Why didn't I know about it?'

Jet grinned. 'I have my methods. Maybe I just took out a pile of old stones and shook them about a bit and asked them to recommend somewhere to eat. Isn't that what you do?'

Cassa made a face at him. She was surprised to find herself relaxing in his company, feeling oddly tranquil as if there had been no difference of opinion between them, as if the uncertainty and aggravation of the previous evening had never happened. She glanced across the little garden table and watched as he studied his menu, noting the firm, straight brows, the cool, clean planes of his cheekbones, the unexpected vigour of his jaw. His eyes were steady, his lips slightly parted; she wondered suddenly what they would feel like to kiss, and turned her head away abruptly, annoyed with herself. Hadn't she already got all the sorted out in her mind? OK, so he was attractive—but physical attraction wasn't everything, and she'd made up her mind, firmly and categorically, that she wasn't going to fall in love with this man. It needed more than cool silvery eyes, more than a curving white grin, more than long, sensitive fingers. . . It needed a mental rapport, an emotional contact. It needed two personalities that could match and compliment each other.

And, with an Aquarius and a Gemini, those conditions would be difficult to meet. Their star signs were against them right from the start.

I don't want to fall in love anyway, she reminded herself. I'm happy as I am. I want to live my own life before I begin to share it with anyone else.

Jet glanced up suddenly and Cassa realised that she was staring at him again. He caught her gaze and lifted his dark golden brows in a quizzical movement, and she blushed—again! she thought crossly—and looked down hastily at her own menu. The young waitress came out from the inn to see if they were ready to order, and Cassa made her selection at random.

'Melon and then chicken with cashews, please,' she said and instantly wished she had chosen whitebait followed by guinea-fowl. And was as quickly glad that she hadn't when Jet made exactly that choice.

As if by common consent, they then turned their conversation to topics far removed from either Elgar or crystals. Jet had a good many entertaining stories to tell of his travels, from those he had made as a child with his parents to his later years, after university, when his restlessness had driven him to remoter parts of the world. 'Mother and Dad always went to cultural centres or large towns, naturally. We never saw the wilder places—the mountains of Alaska, where I watched grizzly bears fishing for salmon, the long empty beaches of Oregon, the stark scenery of Iceland and Labrador—so I was left feeling. . .somewhat unbalanced, in a way. As if I had to add these places to my repertoire of experience in order to become whole. Does that make sense to you?'

'Yes, it does,' Cassa said thoughtfully. She was beginning to feel she might learn to understand this strange man with his lively mind that had to enquire into everything. Wasn't she just a little bit similar herself? Didn't she too want to *know*—to communicate?

But, before she could explore this idea, Jet's darting mind had fastened on something else, and they were away into a different topic, a different direction, into a realm where they found no common ground and were soon arguing and shaking their heads at each other and giving up with laughter that was half mirth and half exasperation, aware that there were some things on which they would never agree.

'Not that it matters,' Jet observed as they went out to the car through the twilight. 'We're two individuals—it wouldn't do at all if we were to agree on everything. There'd be no interest at all.'

'So you find your interest in argument?' Cassa said as she slid into the low-slung seat. 'Don't you think that could get rather wearing?'

'Not at all. And I didn't say anything about arguing. I just find your different point of view refreshing—stimulating.' Instead of starting the engine, he turned and looked at her, then reached out a hand and touched her chin with the tip of one finger. 'You're a very intriguing person, Cassa; do you know that? I thought that by the end of an evening I'd be able to sum you up—I'd know you. But I don't. And I find that very interesting. Very interesting indeed. . .'

Cassa sat quite still, her gaze locked with his, unable

to move as he came closer. His eyes looked deep into hers and once again she had the unnerving sensation that he could look directly into her mind. And then her own eyes closed of their own volition, as his lips brushed against hers.

Time held its breath. The sounds of the evening faded. There was nothing for those few brief seconds, nothing but the coolness of Jet's lips against hers, the feather touch of a mouth that was firm and sweet, yet promised much more. The faintest flavour of something she could not define, something that breathed the essence of his personality and was gone as elusively as gossamer on a September dawn.

Jet took his lips away as gently and delicately as he had laid them against hers, and Cassa took a shivering breath. He touched her face again, his fingertips no more than a whisper against her skin, and then drew back.

'You know, you could drive a man crazy,' he muttered, staring into her eyes. 'Did you know that, Cassa? Do you do it deliberately?'

A flutter of panic caught at her heart. What was happening between them? What was happening to her? She tried to remember her earlier thoughts—hadn't she made up her mind that there could be nothing between them, that physical attraction wasn't enough? What had happened to her resolve?

'Deliberately?' she repeated, and her voice was husky, as if it had not been used for a long time. 'No, I don't do it deliberately, Jet. And I don't believe there's any risk of me or any other girl driving you crazy. You're not the type. You've said it yourself—you don't like commitment. In fact, you're a typical Aquarius—

you want friendship and love-affairs, but you'll never settle to marriage.'

Her voice had warmed as she'd spoken, and she found her thoughts racing ahead, carrying her words further than she'd intended. And she knew she'd gone too far when Jet laughed and moved away.

'Who said anything about marriage? I kissed you, Cassa, that's all—and yes, I find you desirable and exciting—which you know very well. But as for marriage—strictly for the birds; let *them* build their nests. I thought that was pretty clear.'

It was, she wanted to say, and didn't I just say so? But she knew that they would only get into one of those silly and irritating arguments that went 'but you said. . .' and 'ah, but then you said. . .'—which wouldn't get them anywhere. Feeling annoyed with him for putting her in the wrong and no less annoyed with herself for inviting it, she turned away and busied herself with her safety-belt. It was a pity the kiss had ever happened, she thought, and stared determinedly out of the window as Jet drove through the darkening lanes.

All the same, she couldn't help thinking about it, remembering the tender feel of his lips against hers, the gentle sensuality of his mouth, the tiny flickering hint of a flame that could light between them. And the memory was still there when they had said a polite goodnight at the foot of her stairs and she was back in the flat, alone, watching the red glow of his tail-lights disappear in the night.

CHAPTER THREE

FOR the rest of that week Cassa buried herself in her work, accepting some new crystals for the shop, adding a few to her own collection, doing readings for one or two new clients—a fairly new departure for her and something she was beginning to enjoy very much—and spending her evenings either reading at home or walking on the hills.

They had a special quality, the Malvern Hills, she mused as she climbed the wide grassy track up Happy Valley and came to the col from where she could look west across the smaller, rolling hillocks of Herefordshire towards the Welsh Marches. Something healing when you felt low, something joyous when you wanted to be uplifted. No wonder Elgar had found such inspiration for his music here; no wonder some people still believed that, as he had said to one of his friends, 'if you walk on these hills and hear a thread of music, I shall be walking beside you.' It was easy to feel his presence there, striding the hills, hearing music in the breeze and translating it so that everyone could hear the same melody.

Thinking of Elgar brought Jet Tayler back into her mind, and she turned impatiently away from the long, hazy view. Why couldn't she forget him? So he was attractive—he wasn't the only attractive man she'd ever met. So they got on well enough together, as long as they kept off certain topics—the topics that interested them most. That wasn't exactly promising for a good relationship; there were far too many undercurrents, too many opportunities for sparks to start flying.

And who was talking about a relationship anyway? Her face burned as she remembered his words. He'd come to her flat for a meal and what amounted to a business proposition; she'd refused and he'd taken her out the next evening—intending, she had no doubt, to try to persuade her. It hadn't happened, and since then she'd seen and heard nothing of him. End of story.

So forget him, she told herself sternly. And started the last climb to the top of the Worcester Beacon.

There had been a small café here until quite recently. It had been burned down, but the walls still stood while the argument raged as to whether it should be rebuilt. It made a shelter now from the winds that sometimes scoured the bare rounded tops of the hills. Cassa turned at the end of the wall, intending to go and look at the toposcope which indicated all the places that could be seen from this spot—and stopped short, a gasp in her throat, as she almost walked into the arms of the tall man who stood there, smiling at her with a challenge in his eyes.

'Well, hello there, Cassa. Fancy running into you right up here.'

'Jet!' she whispered, and could say no more. It was as if by thinking about him she had conjured him up out of the air. But no—that was ridiculous. Someone as solid as Jet Tayler could only have walked up here under his own power.

'Well, don't look at me as if I were a ghost,' he said cheerfully. 'I'm real—as real as those rocks. Here— feel.' He held out an arm that was covered only by the thin cotton of a shirt-sleeve.

Cassa found her hand lifting towards it. She pulled it back again hastily and caught the gleam of amusement in his eyes. Her cheeks warm, she stuck her hands into the pockets of her jeans.

'You're still in Malvern, then,' she said foolishly, and his grin widened.

'I am, as you see. And enjoying it very much. I like the place. I could almost—almost, I say!—settle here. It's got something.' He looked down at her and the gleam of laughter left his eyes. 'You feel it too.'

It was statement, not a question, but Cassa nodded. 'I always have. There's a soothing quality, a serenity. . . I'm surprised it appeals to you, though. I'd have thought that was the last thing you'd want.'

'Oh, I need soothing just as much as the next man,' he said lightly, and then added, 'I just need the right person to do the soothing. And I haven't found her yet.'

We weren't talking about people. We were talking about places, Cassa thought wildly, but his eyes were on her face and she couldn't answer. After a moment he reached out and laid his hand on her shoulder.

'Cassa,' he said quietly, and then, as she looked down at the grass beneath their feet, 'no—don't turn away. Look at me.'

Reluctantly she raised her eyes to his. The silver-bright colour had softened to the tender glow of moonstones, and she caught her breath. It was as if he were speaking to her, but she either could not or would not hear what he was trying to say.

Why not? she wondered, dazed. Was she afraid? And, if so, what was there to fear?

'Cassa,' he said again in the same quiet tone, 'I feel we've got off on the wrong foot, somehow. We get on so well, and then—it's as if a shutter comes down. Let's start again, shall we? Let's try to be friends.'

'I'm quite happy to be friends with you,' she said stiffly, but he shook his head.

'No. I mean *real* friends. Not just pleasant nodding acquaintances.'

Cassa stared at him. Her mouth was dry, her heart kicking irregularly, like a panicking rabbit. 'What do you want from me, Jet Tayler?' she whispered.

His fingertips tightened on her arm. 'Nothing that you aren't prepared to give me. But—Cassa, can't you understand?—if you'd only let yourself go you'd be happy to give me whatever I asked. There's something—something special between us, and it's something neither of us should deny.' He moved a little closer and she felt the warmth of his body radiating through the thin clothes they both wore, so that it was almost as if the clothes had been wafted away on the breeze, leaving them naked together. 'Give it a chance, Cassa,' he murmured, his voice husky in his throat. 'Let's see what it is, this special feeling we both have. Let's find out. . .'

Cassa stared at him. His eyes were like stars on fire, his fingers burned into her skin. Her heart was racing now, her skin hot, her breasts tingling with the need to be touched. Above them the sky was growing darker, the blue of afternoon fading into the dusky velvet of night. It wheeled around her head and she saw the first early stars as if they were Jet's eyes, gazing at her from every point.

She was aware of her lips parting, soft and trembling, lifted towards him. She was aware of her eyes, closing slowly, of her entire body melting towards him.

'Cassa. . .' he murmured, and once again his lips were on hers.

But there was no tender, delicate brush as if of a moth's wing this time. From the moment his lips touched her mouth she was conscious of an urgent need that pulsed through his body and set alight an answering need in her own. Her heart stopped its racing and leapt, as if to meet his; then she was no longer aware of it, only of a pulsing heat that tore through her trembling body, of a weakness that threatened to overpower her so that she was forced to cling to him with both hands; of a surging desire to press herself against the tall, hard body, to be wrapped warmly in the strong arms that enfolded her, to stay here forever, forever, forever. . .

Jet held her close against him. His lips moved over hers, exploring with a tenderness that was no less passionate for being so gentle, touching the corners of her mouth, before moving away to trace the contours of her face. He planted tiny kisses over both eyes, touching them with exquisite delicacy, let the tip of his tongue move slowly down the line of her nose, moved up again to close her eyes once more with his lips. Cassa turned her face under his, wanting his mouth on hers again, and she felt the soft movement of a laugh in his throat as at last he answered her need and settled his lips against her open mouth.

The world spun as she felt his tongue stroke her lips, parting them a little more, and then slide between them, flicking against the softness of her inner lips, finding the tip of her own tongue and dancing against it, tangling and then twisting with an increasing urgency that had her gasping and trembling in his arms. Her own arms were around his neck, drawing him down against her as she strained to meet him; their bodies were moulding together, matching contour for contour, their shapes a perfect complement. She moved against him, needing something more, feeling a desperation she could not define, knowing that his kiss, devastating though it was, was not enough. There had to be more. . .she needed more. . .

Jet took his lips away and stared down at her. His eyes were opaque now, soft as a pigeon's wing, dark as the dusky sky.

'My God, Cassa,' he breathed, 'do you know what you're doing to me?'

She shook her head. She knew only what he was doing to her, and she wanted more of it. There was nothing in the world but this driving need, this urgent desire that scorched her body. She reached up again for his lips, but he shook his head and put her away from him.

'Not now, Cassa, my sweet,' he muttered. 'And not here. . . There'll come a time, I promise you. But not just yet. . .'

He held her close again, cradling her in his arms like a child while her heart slowed its beating and her senses returned. He was right, she thought, feeling as though she had just begun to awake. It couldn't happen here, nor now. There had to be another time. Another time. . .

And then full realisation of what had been happening, of what could so easily have happened, of what she had been *wanting* to happen struck suddenly into her mind. And she jerked herself out of his arms, staring at him with all her old panic in her eyes.

'Cassa! Don't look like that—I'm not going to hurt you———'

'You're not going to do *anything* to me!' she exclaimed, putting several feet of space between them with one spring. 'I don't know what I was thinking of——'

'I do!' he interrupted, grinning.

'I must have gone mad—there's a full moon somewhere—I was out of my mind—it meant nothing, *nothing*.' She backed against the old wall, feeling the rough stones like reality under her hands. 'You understand that, don't you, Jet? It meant nothing—and it's never going to happen again.'

He stared at her curiously. 'Cassa, what's got into you? It was a kiss, that's all. And you might recall that *I* stopped it—not you. You can't accuse me of trying to take advantage of you—that's something I'd never do. But if you let a man kiss you that way, and you kiss him back, *that way*—you must expect whatever you get. Not many men are made of stone, Cassa.'

She lifted a hand to her burning face. 'I know. I told you, I don't know what I was thinking of. I never meant anything like that to happen; I——'

'Don't make such a production of it,' he advised easily. 'It was a kiss—nothing more than that. We'll forget it ever happened, if that makes you happier. But—my God, Cassa, I wish I knew just what makes you tick. One minute you take off like a rocket, the next you're playing the blushing virgin. How's a man supposed to know how you want to be treated?'

'Just treat me like a person,' she said, her voice steadier now, although she knew she was behaving erratically. But wasn't that a Gemini all over? It had always been one of her characteristics—or so her friends told her. Her behaviour seemed perfectly reasonable to her, following the processes of her mind—but it didn't seem to strike other people that way. Just as it didn't seem to strike Jet as being reasonable now.

Well, that was his problem. She turned away, looking for the path in the fading light, and Jet followed her. They walked for a while in silence.

'I meant what I said, Cassa,' he said presently. 'About starting again, trying to build up a friendship. I didn't actually mean in quite that way—I got carried away too. But if you think we could still be friends. . .'

'Why?' she asked with a hint of desperation in her voice. 'Why should we even try? What can we be to each other, Jet? You're not going to be here long. You'll go away, and what then? All that effort will have been for nothing.'

'Well, I'd hope it wouldn't be too much effort!' he said with a smile in his voice. 'But I still have this feeling that there's something between us that shouldn't be ignored, Cassa. And I hate to pass up friendship. Surely it's never "for nothing"?'

She stopped on the path and faced him. Below them, the lights were beginning to sparkle on the plain.

'So it has to be on your terms. Friendship—nothing more. Whatever I might come to feel.' She stopped, realising how her words might betray her. 'Not that I expect to feel anything at all,' she added quickly.

An expression flickered across Jet's face, but it was too dim now to see what it was. Quietly, he said, 'I didn't think anything more was likely, Cassa. I thought that was one area in which we did agree.'

She bit her lip. 'Yes, it is,' she said after a moment. 'Yes.'

'So what's wrong with friendship?' He caught at her

hand and held it loosely. 'Would it be such a risk, Cassa? Would it be such a waste of time?'

Yes, it would be a risk, she thought, looking up at the grey eyes. It's a risk I'd be mad to take. A risk I dare not take.

But that was something she could not say. She could only shake her head mutely.

'So we'll try again, yes?' His voice was soft, impossible to deny. 'We'll be friends, you and I. Friends—and nothing more.'

'Yes.' Her voice sounded cracked, as if it came from a throat too dry to form the words. 'Yes, we'll be friends.'

He gave a sudden laugh of pure triumph and tucked her hand underneath his arm, swinging her away down the path.

'Right! We'll start tomorrow. You have an assistant in that shop of yours, don't you?'

'Yes, but——'

'We'll have a day out together,' he declared. 'I'll nip into the delicatessen and stock up, then I'll call for you in the shop—say about eleven? It's going to be another fine day. There's a place I want to see and then we'll go walking.' His voice rang cheerfully through the trees as they descended the hill. He sounded as if they'd been friends for years, as if nothing out of the ordinary had happened to them at all. And maybe it hadn't as far as he was concerned, Cassa thought bewilderedly. Maybe that kiss was nothing at all to him.

But she knew that it had meant a good deal to her. She knew that she would remember it and savour it again in those memories. She knew that the very thought of it would bring that same warmth to her heart, that same tingle to her body.

She wasn't at all sure she'd been wise to agree to being friends with Jet Tayler. But what else could she have done?

By eleven next morning Cassa had definitely decided that she wasn't going out with Jet Tayler. Whether he wanted plain friendship or not, this was a relationship that had no future and there was no point at all in wasting any more time on it. Consequently, instead of the jeans and shirt she might have worn in anticipation of a day out that included a picnic and walk, she wore a floral skirt and pink T-shirt with sandals that left her feet almost bare. Round her neck she hung her favourite crystal, and when she arrived at the shop she immediately began to unpack and sort a new delivery of stones.

'Oh, they're nice!' exclaimed Suky, her assistant, coming in just as she had them piled on the counter. 'Jaspers—look, here's a lovely light green; isn't it perfect? The stone of happiness—just how I feel this morning!'

She laid the stone back on the counter, where its gold-green light shimmered in the sun, and went through to the back room. Cassa looked at the stone which Suky had picked out, realising that she had not even noticed it. And then she looked at the stones she had separated from the others as she had begun to sort them.

There was a large stone which seemed to contain several different colours—red, yellow and green, as if all the jaspers had come together in debate or conciliation. The variegated jasper—the stone which denoted anxiety, worries about the affairs of the heart, an effort to hide from emotional hurt. Cassa stared at it for several moments.

She looked at the others. Two red, signifying deep emotion, a dark green which spoke of emotional rejection, a second, smaller variegated stone which reinforced that first cry of anxiety, and an assortment of others, red and dark green, all saying the same things. . . Stones that had come almost unbidden into her fingers, as if they had chosen themselves. And she heard her own voice, saying to a client who had come to her for a reading, 'You'll see what you're meant to see. Just pick whichever stones seem to say something to you.'

Cassa took a deep breath. This was no full reading, for she had only jaspers here, so had had no opportunity to pick others, such as agates, tiger's eye or quartz. Nevertheless, there must be some reason why she had picked out only these stones and not touched the light greens which signified the bubbling happiness of her assistant Suky, or the pretty pink and grey which showed the influence of an older man.

For an instant her thoughts flew to Jet Tayler. He was older—but no, even if she had picked that stone it wouldn't have represented him. The pink and grey represented a man of another generation—and Jet was hardly that. She guessed that he was no more than ten or twelve years older than herself. And none of the stones had shown the presence of another person anyway—they had all been involved with her own emotions.

But what emotions. . .? She looked at them again, at the anxiety and vulnerability they showed her. And for a moment she was tempted to go to her own tray of stones, the tumbled pile of a hundred and fifty or so

which she used for readings, and pick out the full
number of nine to see just what happened.

No. She would not do that. It was useless to try to
do your own reading. You knew what the stones
meant, you knew what your own feelings and hopes
and fears were, you could not prevent yourself even
subconsciously picking out those that you wanted to
choose. You could never get an accurate reading for
yourself.

This had happened by accident, and meant nothing
without at least the choice of agates and amethysts and
quartzes that lay with the jaspers in her own tray. It
wasn't even half a reading. She hadn't even been
choosing—merely sorting a new delivery. It meant
nothing. Nothing.

All the same, she could not forget those warnings:
the hint of barriers being erected to save her from pain,
the barriers that could also prevent joy. Was she really
doing that? Was she really cutting herself off from
happiness—simply because she'd been hurt once
before?

Quickly and efficiently, Cassa sorted the rest of the
stones and arranged them in one of the cabinets. She
lingered over this task, which was the one she enjoyed
most in the whole shop. Her hands moved lovingly
over the crystals that lay this way and that, their facets
catching and reflecting the light, on their bed of black
velvet. She picked up an amethyst, angling it to get the
best of its deep purple beauty, then laid it down and
lifted a citrine quartz. Its dark barley-sugar brown
crystals seemed to grow from the clear quartz at its
root, like the model of a tiny castle growing from ice.
She gazed at it, feeling a strange affinity with it, not
wanting to put it back.

'New beginnings,' Suky said softly in her ear. 'It's a lovely stone, isn't it?' And Cassa looked at her, startled, and then found that her fingers had tightened around the crystal as if she could not bear to let it go.

New beginnings. . . What did it mean for her? Anything? Or nothing?

'Oh, there was a phone call for you just now,' Suky remarked, starting to tidy up the bookshelves. 'I didn't disturb you—he said just to give you a message, and I could see you were busy. Someone called Jet—at least, that's what it sounded like. He asked me to tell you that he wouldn't be able to meet you at the shop after all, but could you come up to St Ann's Well at about eleven? He's doing some sort of research and arranged to meet someone there—he said you'd understand.'

'Oh, *did* he?' Cassa's strange mood disappeared and she felt healthily angry. 'Well, I hope you told him I was busy.'

'Well, no, I didn't.' Suky looked disturbed. 'Should I have? He seemed to think it was all arranged—thanked me for looking after the shop for the day so you could go out. He sounded very nice,' she added apologetically.

'I'm sure he did.' Cassa's voice was grim. 'Oh, never mind, Suky, it's not your fault and it doesn't matter anyway. I suppose I'll have to go, if only to tell him that I'm not going out for the day after all. There's far too much to do here.'

'Is there?' Suky looked round the shop. 'It all looks fine to me.' She hesitated, then said, 'Look, it's none of my business, Cassa, but why don't you go? He did sound very nice—and you've been looking a bit tired lately. I think you need some time off.'

Time off, yes, Cassa thought. Time off with Jet

Tayler—like a hole in the head. But she could hardly say that without arousing the other girl's curiosity, and, good friends though they were, she didn't really want to discuss Jet now. She looked at Suky, then shrugged and grinned a little ruefully.

'Oh, all right. I suppose it won't do any harm. And we aren't really very busy. I might as well go.'

Suky laughed. 'And there speaks a real enthusiast! You know, Cassa, you really haven't been having enough fun lately. You go and enjoy yourself before you forget how. You're a fun person—had you forgotten that?'

Maybe I had, Cassa thought later as she took the little road that went up beside the Unicorn Inn and then the steep, zigzag path that led to St Ann's Well. Here, for years, people had climbed to collect pure Malvern water from the spring which gushed into a large, shallow bowl set in the hillside and protected by the octagonal building which was now a coffee shop. It wasn't the only place where Malvern water—so pure that it contained 'nothing at all'—could be collected; there were several others around the hills. But it was probably the most famous.

Almost as a ritual, Cassa scooped up a few mouthfuls of cool water, sipping some and sprinkling the rest over her hot cheeks. She needed all her coolness before meeting Jet Tayler—but, once again, he caught her by surprise by coming up behind her as she splashed her face and laying his long, tapering hand casually on her bent back.

'Hi there, Cassa. So you got my message. I was half afraid you'd decide not to come.'

She straightened, her heart thudding, and turned to face him. 'Why ever should I do that?'

'Don't ask me,' he said, grinning. 'I've given up trying to divine your reasons for doing anything. It just seemed in character, that's all.'

'You mean I'm the type to stand a man up if I feel like it.' She was uncomfortably aware that this was just what she'd been inclined to do, and even more uncomfortably aware that Jet knew it. 'Well, here I am, so you were wrong, weren't you?'

He half tilted his head and smiled at her, and once again she wished he didn't have quite such a devastating smile. It seemed to curve wickedly over his whole face, lighting up the silver-grey eyes which crinkled so attractively at the corners, and—hastily, she jerked her mind away and concentrated resolutely on their surroundings.

'Pleasant here, isn't it?' she chattered brightly. 'I think they must do a very good trade in the little coffee shop. And you can have a party in the bar upstairs, which would be fun, wouldn't it? Lots of people come up here on Sunday mornings. The sun's warm here even in winter; it's a real little haven, a sun-trap. . .' Her voice trailed away as she caught his eyes resting quizzically on her face. 'Well, there's no need to look at me like that,' she ended crossly.

Jet laughed. 'That's more like my Cassa! Prickly as a little hedgehog. The bright social bit isn't you somehow, is it? What's the matter? Come over shy?' He grinned as if he knew just what the matter was, and Cassa was furious to feel herself blushing yet again. What *was* it about this man?

'I'm not prickly,' she defended herself. 'You must expect a girl to get cross if you keep on teasing the way you do. I feel like a—a specimen you're examining. Like something under a microscope.'

His grin widened. 'I told you—you intrigue me. I just can't pin you down. But it's fun trying, all the same.'

'And now you make me sound like a butterfly!' Already she was wishing she hadn't come. She'd have been better off to have stayed in the shop, chatting with Suky, helping customers choose crystals, arranging the hanging prisms to create rainbows all around the shop. . . She walked past Jet and out into the sunshine, sitting down on one of the benches that were terraced round the octagonal building to form something like a small amphitheatre.

'I'd quite like a coffee, if it's not too much trouble,' she said haughtily, and Jet bowed exaggeratedly.

'Your wish is my command.' He went inside to collect it and Cassa looked after him. If only her wish were his command! But if it were—what would she wish? The memory of his kisses burned her cheeks and lips again and she turned her mind hastily away.

'So where are we going?' she asked when he brought the coffee out. 'Is the picnic still on?'

Jet glanced at her outfit. 'Well, the picnic, maybe, but you don't look dressed for a country ramble. Far too Laura Ashley—floating through buttercup-filled fields seems to be more your style today. So I suppose we could do that instead.'

'Except that it's not your style,' Cassa observed, but he smiled and shook his head.

'You'd be surprised what I can enjoy when I'm in the mood—and in the right company. Now, what I had in mind was a visit to Broadheath—to Elgar's birthplace. It's on my itinerary, and the countryside around it is very pretty. Some French bread and cheese, a few olives and a glass of wine in one of those fields, and who wants to go for a walk?' His eyes moved over her lazily and she shivered. 'What do you say?'

Cassa wanted to say no, but somehow her tongue wouldn't co-operate. She looked away and gazed down into her coffee. What was she doing, sitting here with this man? What was she doing agreeing to go out with him?

Yet it did sound delightful. . . .

'Elgar's birthplace?' she said, fastening on the only concrete information he had given her. 'So you're still interested in writing your biography?'

'Of course. Whyever not?' His brows lifted in that mannerism she was coming to know so well. 'Just because you won't let me see the letters——'

'You're not going to persuade me,' she said quickly.

'I'm not going to try. I was merely going to say that the whole project doesn't revolve around a few letters that may or may not be interesting. There's plenty more to say about Elgar. I intend that my work will be different from any previous one, anyway, letters or no letters.' He paused. 'Incomplete though it may be without them.'

'You *are* trying to persuade me!' she flashed, and he grinned as if he'd caught her out.

'All right, little firebrand, don't get worried. It must be clear even to you that without all the available information any biography must be incomplete. That's a simple fact.'

'And exactly why I don't approve of biographies anyway,' she said. 'How can you ever be sure that what you've written *is* complete, or accurate? It could be overturned next day by the discovery of yet more evidence. But the readers aren't necessarily going to know that. They'll read your book and take your word for it—and carry a wrong idea of the person for the rest of their lives.'

'It happens,' he acknowledged. 'Which is why there's room for a new biography of any public figure roughly every ten years—to take account of new discoveries, new thinking. And why one should always, of course, read the latest before making any judgements.' He unfolded himself and rose to his feet. 'Finished your coffee? Why don't we go?'

He strolled away down the path without waiting for her acquiescence, and Cassa scrambled to her feet and began to hurry after him—and then stopped and went on more slowly. Why should she run after him like a puppy-dog anyway? She'd take her time. He'd wait, if he really wanted her company.

Het had parked his BMW on St Ann's road, below the zigzag path which led to the well. He was waiting when Cassa sauntered down, leaning casually against the bonnet, gazing up into the leafy trees as if he had all the time in the world. And when she arrived beside him he barely glanced at her; just put his finger to his lips to motion her to silence.

Cassa opened her mouth and closed it again. Jet's head was tilted as if he was listening, and she became aware of the birdsong that rang from the branches. Blackbird, thrushes, birds she could not identify—all were calling their joy from the treetops, filling the air with music. Had Elgar stood here once, leaning against a treetrunk perhaps, listening to the ancestors of these same birds and weaving their song into his music?

Jet moved at last and opened the door for Cassa to get in. He didn't speak as he drove down to the main road, and neither did she. In a silence that was more companionable than she had expected, they left Malvern and headed towards Worcester.

Broadheath lay three miles away from the city, its common making an unexpectedly wide space of green among the narrow lanes and fields. A country pub stood close to the cottage where Elgar had been born, and here Jet parked his car so that they could walk along the lane and through the gate into the small, secluded garden.

'There are the tombstones to his dogs,' Cassa pointed out. 'Just in there, through the bushes. Mina and Marco. And this is the stable his father built for the pony.'

They went in through the door and Jet paid the entrance fee. He had told Cassa that he liked to visit such places incognito in the first instance, not saying that he was interested in research, just to get to feel for the atmosphere that greeted any visitor. And there was certainly atmosphere here; Elgar's own music greeted them as they wandered in, and went with them through the tiny rooms. It surrounded them as it had surrounded the composer himself, except that for them it came from a recording; for him it had sounded in his head.

'There are so many mementoes here,' Cassa remarked as they prowled around the study. Elgar had never actually worked here—he had left the cottage with his family when he was only two years old—but it had been his wish that it should be the place where he was remembered, and it seemed as if he must have spent his life here, in spirit if not in person. 'Look at his desk—all these bits and pieces that must have meant a lot to him. His pipes, his score sheets, his spectacles—things he used every day of his life. It's as if he'd just got up to go out for a moment and would be back at any minute.'

'Yet, as he never worked here and there can be only a few of the things he used during his whole lifetime, it can't be an accurate picture,' Jet said slyly.

'Oh, but it gives you a *feel* for him,' Cassa said earnestly. 'I feel I know him, just from seeing these things and——' She caught his sardonic eye and broke off. 'All right—I know what you're saying. It's like a biography—you may not see the whole picture but you can——'

'You can see a glimmer of the truth,' he said as she hesitated. 'Isn't that at least something, Cassa? Isn't it worth striving for—a glimmer of the truth?'

She did not answer. Instead, she walked around the room, looking at the pictures of Elgar, the portraits, the photographs that showed him as a young man, a man of middle age, elderly.

'He looks a nice man,' she said after a while. 'Such a straight, direct look. And he had a sense of humour, too—look at those eyes, and the lines around them. You only get them from laughing.'

'And that's exactly what I want to show,' Jet said, coming to her side. 'The humour of the man and his music. The *Variations*—there's such fun in them. The little dog, the stammer in the voice of the young girl, the way one person walks and another scurries. He did something nobody had ever done before—he painted portraits in music. And that wasn't all. He loved words, Cassa—look at these crossword-puzzle books, look at the anagrams he made of his name and his wife's and daughter's to call their house Craeg Lea. Not only that, his daughter's name itself, Carice, is a part anagram of

his wife's—Caroline Alice. He got both fun and satis-
faction out of that. He enjoyed life—he must have
done. There was nothing stuffy about Edward Elgar.'

'No.' Cassa had come to a story written by Elgar and
printed in the *Tail-Wagger*—a story about a puppy.
'No, there wasn't. He must have been lovely to know.'

'And I'd like to help people to know him better,' Jet
said softly in her ear.

Cassa stood quite still. She knew very well what Jet
was trying to do. He was trying to make her change
her mind. She turned and looked up into his face.

'I won't show you the letters, Jet,' she said quietly.
'Elgar wrote that music as an enigma. He intended it
to be a mystery. And I won't do anything to spoil that.'

Jet looked into her eyes and she saw a slight change
somewhere deep in his gaze. Then he inclined his head.

'Very well, Cassa. I accept that. But. . .wouldn't you
like to *know*? Yourself, I mean? Just to know that you
and you alone held the secret?'

Cassa hesitated. The thought of the letters hung in
her mind. She could picture them, still in the old box
where her father had discovered them. She imagined
herself taking them out one by one, unfolding the
yellowing paper, reading the words that had been
written over a hundred years ago.

'You would like to know,' he whispered. 'Anyone
would. . .'

'No!' she said firmly and a shade too loudly. 'No, I
don't want to know. It's their business, Jet, not ours.
Leave it alone.' She turned away, feeling suddenly
upset and near to tears. 'I wish the letters had never
been found!' she burst out, and walked quickly into the
next room.

They looked around the rest of the cottage in silence.

Cassa struggled with her emotions, unable to understand just why she felt so distressed. It was all over, all
in the past—why should it affect her so much now? Or
was that what was affecting her anyway? Was it something else, something very much in the present? Like
the proximity of Jet Tayler, the fire that ran through
her whenever he came near, the tingle somewhere low
down in her body when he touched or looked at her?

Once again she wondered just why she was here.
Hadn't she set out from home that morning determined
not to come out with Jet? Hadn't she made up her
mind there was no future in any kind of relationship
with him? So how had it come about that she was here,
in this small cottage so redolent of the man Jet wanted
to write about? How had it happened that she had
agreed—almost without realising it—to spend the day
with him?

I'm crazy, she thought, watching the sun slant in
through the small windows and turn Jet's russet hair to
a burnished gold. I seem to have lost control of my
own senses. And she made a determined effort to
regain that control, telling herself again and again, as
she had told herself that first evening, I'm not falling in
love. I'm not. I'm *not*.

CHAPTER FOUR

THEY walked back to the pub in silence. Cassa nodded briefly when Jet suggested a drink before they left. She sat at one of the tables outside, feeling the sunshine warm on her bare arms, her eyes closed.

By the time Jet came out with the glasses she felt she had regained her composure. It was nothing more than a passing physical attraction, after all—the sort of thing any healthy young woman might feel when she was feeling a bit lonely. The word 'unloved' came into her mind, the lost emotion of rejection signified by the dark green stone she had picked out only that morning. Unloved. But that was ridiculous! Why should she feel unloved?

There are plenty of people who love me, she thought fiercely. Plenty. There are Mum and Dad, even if they are thousands of miles away. There's Brian and his family. There are my friends—Suky and the others. There are a lot of people I love and who love me.

But there was one who didn't, a small inner voice reminded her. One who said he loved you, yet proved that he didn't. . .

Cassa opened her eyes abruptly, banishing the image on her mind. She found herself looking almost directly at the sun, and flinched away from its brightness. And then a shadow blocked it from her view and she looked up into Jet's face.

'Are you all right, Cassa? You look a bit bemused.'

'I think I must have been dozing,' she said, taking

the glass of cool golden liquid from him. 'Oh—St Clement's; that's lovely. It's the sun—it's so warm.'

'Perhaps we're in for a hot summer,' Jet said, sitting down opposite her so that his face was still shaded. 'Sounds good to me. I'm a lizard in the sun. How about you?'

'Mmm, I love it. I had a holiday once, in Greece——' She stopped abruptly. 'Did you get all the information you needed here, Jet? Or will you need to come back?'

'Oh, I'll have to come back. I want to study things in detail—I'll arrange with the curator for some private study.' Jet leaned back in his chair and sipped his beer. 'I just wanted to get atmosphere this morning—and you helped a lot with that.'

'I did?' She felt unaccountably pleased. 'How?'

'Oh, just by your reactions. Your feelings about Elgar himself, about this place. The way you noticed his humour, the feeling you had that he must have been "lovely to know". Most people just think of him as a composer. You saw another dimension.'

'But surely most people who come to this cottage see that too? It's there for anyone.'

'Anyone with the right eyes,' Jet said quietly. 'Not everyone has those eyes. It's the task of the biographer to look at his subject with as complete a vision as possible, and convey what he sees.'

Cassa set down her drink with a tiny thump. Here they were again, back at the old argument. But this time she wasn't going to be baited. She was beginning to realise that Jet was the kind of man who went all out for what he wanted—who would never be satisfied with half a loaf when the entire baker's shop stood at his disposal. She felt a sudden quiver of excitement at the thought—what sort of a lover would such a man make?

Not that she was ever likely to find out! Jet Tayler had made it clear that he wasn't interested in long-term commitments. He was a typical Aquarius in that, and you couldn't change a man's nature. Even if you wanted to.

And I don't want to, she reminded herself firmly. Aquarius and Gemini—air with air? Oh, we might seem to have the same kind of viewpoint, but we'd spend our entire time discussing things in circles, and never getting to the point. I need earth to pin me down, or fire to keep me alive. And, of all the air signs, anyway, Aquarius is the *last* one I need. The very last.

'Shall we go?' Jet had finished his drink and was looking pointedly at Cassa's still half-full glass. 'I'm getting hungry after all this atmosphere-gathering.'

'Sorry—yes, of course.' Cassa finished her drink, savouring the refreshing orange and lemon taste, and followed him to his car. 'Have you anywhere in mind for our picnic?'

'Oh, we're bound to find somewhere pleasant among all these lanes and meadows,' he said easily, and sure enough they had not gone far when he pulled in by a small bridge and led Cassa along beside a shallow stream to the shade of a swooping willow tree. 'How will this do?'

'It's perfect.' She spread the plaid rug and Jet laid out the provisions he had brought. 'Mm—I can see where you've been! Pheasant pâté—olives—pitta bread—Brie—you must have asked someone just what I'd like! And fruit and wine as well.'

'Afraid you credit me with more generosity than I possess,' he said lazily. 'I simply chose the things *I* like. But maybe that just shows what similar tastes we have.'

Cassa caught the note in his voice and looked at him. He was half lying on the grass, leaning on one elbow, looking up at her with eyes crinkled against the sun. Something in his expression seemed to catch at her heart, as if he had plucked at one of its strings. She could almost hear the plangent note that quivered through her body.

Unsought, the memory of last night's kiss on the hills came darkly into her mind. For a moment she was back in his arms, feeling their muscular power wrapping her body close with his. And she knew that he was sharing her memory, that his thoughts were walking with hers.

Slowly, lazily, almost casually, Jet reached up a long arm and twisted his hand behind her neck. He drew her down to him and Cassa went, unresisting, feeling an inevitability that drained her of all thought, left her only with a deep, warm, sensual need. A need to be in this man's arms, to be touched and held, to be kissed. A need to be loved. . .

Somewhere deep inside, a warning bell sounded, but its note was tiny and far away, too remote to be attended to. It was no more than a breath of a summer breeze against finest crystal, a shiver of sound, and as Cassa parted her lips for Jet's kiss she knew that any warning must go unheeded against the power of the attraction he exerted over her.

'That's better,' he murmured against her mouth. 'That's my Cassa. . .my sweet, lovely Cassa. . .' And his lips were soft against hers, moving slowly, sensuously over hers, tasting their sweetness, exploring their softness, shaping them to the increasing firmness of his own. 'Cassa,' he breathed, his tongue whispering against hers. 'Cassa. . .'

Cassa's mind whirled. She was spinning somewhere out in space, out of control, her heart and pulses thundering in her quivering body, her skin alive to his touch. She felt his hands move slowly over her, exploring the shape of her, and she responded with her own movements. One hand slid down her back, barely touching the thin fabric of her T-shirt, and Cassa felt a tingle in her spine that brought her moving closer against him, an involuntary movement as he brushed across a spot that she had never before realised was so responsive. His fingertips were like feathers, hardly touching her skin, and she could feel each tiny hair of her body rise to meet them, each pore opening to his caress. And all the while his lips were moving over hers, his mobile tongue flicking against them, entering her mouth to play with hers, the kiss growing deeper and ever more intimate as his hands and fingers continued their gentle but insistent exploration.

They were stretched out together on the rug now, their picnic forgotten. The sun was warm on Cassa's face as she lay with her eyes closed, receiving and returning his kisses, responding to his silky caress. Jet was half lying over her, his head bent to hers, the hard strength of his body aligned with her soft suppleness. He lifted his head away slightly, then began to plant small, feather-light kisses all over her face. He took the lobes of her ears between gentle teeth, let his lips trail down her neck, drew softly on the fine skin in the hollow of her throat. He slid one hand from under her back to cup her breast, lifting its fullness towards him, laying his mouth against the softness that he could find at the neck of her T-shirt.

'You're beautiful, Cassa,' he muttered, bringing his mouth up to her hair. 'You're lovely. . .so soft, so smooth that I could stroke you forever. Cassa. . .' His voice was becoming more urgent and her blood leapt to meet the desire in his husky tone. 'Cassa. . .'

There was no mistaking the question in his voice. Cassa was past all reason. The blood was humming through her veins, her skin felt as though it were alive with music, with the melody of love that sang in her heart. Somewhere she could hear sounds, as of trees rustling in the wind or waves crashing on the shore—the sounds that always denoted love when portrayed in films or books. But this was no film, no book—this was real, it was life, and it was happening to her now. All she had to do was say yes. . .

She opened her eyes slowly, drowsily, and looked up into Jet's face. He was gazing down at her, his eyes dark as rain-clouds now, heavy with the hint of a storm about to break. For a moment, or for an eternity, they looked deep into one another's hearts and minds. And then Jet glanced briefly away. She saw his eyes widen, caught the change of expression on his face, felt his body stiffen over hers. And then, astoundingly, saw the laughter break and felt the quiver of mirth run through him.

'Jet!' she exclaimed. 'What——?'

But before she could say more he was drawing her into a sitting position, pointing, his whole body shaking. And she looked around and saw what he had seen.

About forty cows, red and white as in a nursery rhyme, were standing around them in a wide, staring circle. The sight of their curious white faces, their uncomprehending stares, their puzzled brown eyes, was too comical for Cassa not to laugh too. The cows backed away a little, evidently disconcerted by this peculiar human reaction. They looked at each other, pawed the ground, hesitated. And Jet held Cassa in his arms without any sensuality at all now as she laid her head on his chest and almost sobbed with laughter.

'Thank goodness you're not one of those girls who are afraid of cows,' Jet said at last. 'What shall we do—move somewhere else? Or don't you mind eating your lunch under the gaze of forty pairs of bovine eyes?'

'I think they're going away now,' Cassa said as the cows, evidently growing bored, began to move slowly off across the field. 'They seem slightly disappointed.'

Jet gave her a quizzical glance. 'They're not the only ones,' he murmured. 'Cassa. . .'

But Cassa had had time to recover herself, and was already beginning to feel the shock of what had been happening, what could so easily have happened. What on earth had possessed her? she asked herself. What was it that seemed to drive her into this man's arms and behave as if she had no will of her own? Why couldn't she resist him?

'Cassa——'

'Don't say anything, Jet,' she said quickly. 'It was a moment of madness for us both. Let's leave it at that. Let's just make sure it doesn't happen again.' She saw him staring at her and added, 'We just seem to have this unfortunate effect on each other—but now we know about it we can make sure it doesn't get a chance to—to. . .' Her voice faded. 'Jet, don't *look* at me like that. . .'

'*Unfortunate effect*?' he repeated. 'Cassa, there was nothing "unfortunate" about that little encounter. Don't tell me you didn't enjoy it just as much as I did!'

Cassa felt her face flame. Enjoy it! Was 'enjoy' the word for that soaring sensation, that feeling of spinning somewhere out into space, that singing of her blood and skin. . .? But she couldn't say any of that to Jet. She couldn't even let him guess at it.

'That's got nothing to do with it,' she said, hoping her voice sounded as firm as she meant it to. 'I said "unfortunate effect" and that's just what I meant. Look, you've been perfectly honest with me and I appreciate it. You've told me you're not interested in commitment, only in friendship. So——'

'And is a kiss in a meadow on a warm sunny day a "commitment"?' he asked. 'Can't it be friendly? As a matter of fact, I thought that kiss was just about the most friendly I'd ever experienced. Are you telling me it meant more to you?'

Cassa flinched away from the challenge in his voice. How was she to answer this? Tell him yes, it did mean more than mere friendship to her? That would be tantamount to telling him she was in love with him— and that was something she wasn't prepared to admit even to herself. Yet, if she was to shrug and dismiss it as nothing more than a pleasant dalliance, wasn't she telling him something else about herself? Something that was not only unture—that she was the kind of girl who thought nothing of a casual sexual encounter without love—but which could also draw her into deeper trouble. For Jet Tayler was clearly the kind of man who *did* enjoy a casual encounter. And was all too willing to enjoy one with her.

Jet was watching her closely. He moved a little and laid his hand over hers in the warm grass.

'Did it mean more to you, Cassa?' he asked quietly. 'Are you interested in a commitment?'

She stared down at their fingers, entwined together among the green stems. There was something important about the moment, something she could not quite grasp. She repeated his question in her mind. *Was* she interested in a commitment with this man, whom she scarcely knew yet felt at times so tranquil with. . .and at other times so fiery. . .and, yet again, so bewildered?

She jerked her hand away, shifting so that there was a distance between them, so that he could not sway her with the magnetism of his nearness.

No, she could not open her heart to him only to have it rebuffed. She could not take rejection—not again.

'Commitment?' she said, and her voice was pitched a little higher than she liked. 'Of course I'm not interested in a commitment! I've got far too much in my life to want any more complications. And if I were——' she flung him a glance of what she hoped was scorn '—there are plenty of men ahead of you in the queue, Jet Tayler! Don't imagine that just because I happen to have had a couple of evenings free this week I don't have any social life. I just like to keep a bit of space for myself, that's all.' She brushed back her short dark hair with a gesture that was as casual as she could make it. 'Now, are we going to have this picnic or aren't we? The cows have lost interest in us now.'

Jet looked at her. There was an expression somewhere deep in his eyes that she couldn't quite fathom. She felt again that odd sensation, as if he had plucked at the strings of her heart. And then a cloud passed over the sun, and his eyes were veiled, and he turned away.

'Yes, let's eat.' His voice was flat. 'And I suggest we don't take too long over it. Fields with cows in are liable to accumulate certain—well, shall we say, certain characteristics? I don't imagine these have been in here for long, or we'd have noticed before, but with three or four dozen of the creatures ambling around we're bound to start noticing pretty soon!'

Cassa laughed, though her laughter was a little forced, and began to unwrap the food. Jet had also brought some plates and glasses, and soon they were sitting side by side on the rug—each equally careful not to allow their bodies to touch, Cassa thought with a mixture of relief and regret—and eating the pâté spread on the pitta bread.

Neither of them spoke. They sat silently eating, watching the water flow over the stones, watching the sun throw its dappling light through the ripples listening to the rustle of the willow leaves above them. The sun beat warmly down on their heads and soaked gently into their bodies.

It's a perfect afternoon for love, Cassa thought. And felt a sudden bleak loneliness. And remembered again the dark green stone that had almost climbed into her hand that morning.

The stone of rejection.

Their walk was not mentioned again. They drove slowly back to Malvern through the meandering lanes, keeping off the main roads. The Malvern Hills, their whale-back shape unmistakable, loomed above the trees and then disappeared around the next corner, only to appear again from a different angle further along the road. Small black and white cottages dozed in the sunshine amid orchards that were white with a snowstorm of blossom; farms stood back from the road, long, low buildings where even the animals seemed to be enjoying a siesta. They met only a few other vehicles, and the villages of Bosbury and Cradley seemed to be deserted.

At last they were back in Malvern. Jet drew up outside the house where Cassa lived. He looked at her for a moment.

'Thank you for coming with me, Cassa,' he said, and she had a curious feeling that he was saying more. 'It really was a great help.'

'I'm glad,' she answered politely, feeling a pain deep inside that she couldn't understand, was perhaps afraid to understand. 'If you need any more help at any time—though I'm not sure what else I can do. . .' It was her heart, beginning to break, she thought suddenly, and thrust the thought away. Why? Why should it be breaking?

Jet moved suddenly. 'You know very well what else you can do,' he said with an unexpected roughness in his voice. 'Cassa——'

'I won't let you see the letters.' She had to break in on him, had to say that for fear of what he might be about to ask. 'I've told you, Jet, it's no use. You'll have to write your book without them.'

'The letters. . .' He stared at her, and she fumbled with the lock, struggling to open the door before either of them could say more. She was afraid, desperately afraid, of the look in his eyes, the tone of his voice; of his strength, his magnetism, of the power he had over her. 'Cassa, I wasn't——'

But his words were lost as she opened the door and scrambled out. She knew now what he'd been going to say. It was goodbye. He'd been telling her, underneath his words, telling her with his eyes, with his tone, that he was not going to see her again. And that was why her heart had begun to break.

She muttered something and ran through the gateway, ran to the steps that led up the outside of the house to her flat. Her heart hammering, she fitted her key into the lock, pushed open the door and flung herself inside. Only when the door was safely closed behind her did she begin to feel safe.

Safe? she thought with a sob of hysteria. How could she ever feel safe again, when she had to admit the truth now, could evade it no longer? When she had to acknowledge, if only to herself, that she had done what all along she had known she must never do?

She had fallen in love with Jet Tayler. With an Aquarian who ran true to his sign, who didn't want commitment. With a man who would never look on her as anything other than a friend.

There would never be safety for her now. For she had lost her heart.

Later that day, much later, as the sun went behind the Malvern Hills and dusk settled on the little town, Cassa went down to her parents' part of the house. She walked softly about the empty rooms, watering the plants, touching the ornaments, stopping to look at family photographs. Why did she feel so cold, so lost? Why did she feel that there was no one she could turn to, no one who loved her? Why did she feel that something precious, something valuable, had slipped through her fingers?

She stood at the window, gazing out over the plain, watching the lights appear. Some time, years ago, when the century was young—no, earlier than that even, before her grandparents had been born, before her great-grandfather had learned to crawl, in this very room perhaps—a man had come strolling down Abbey

Road with his violin case tucked under his arm. A man with straight brows and humorous, kindly eyes, a man who had loved his friends, even his dogs, enough to immortalise them in music. A man who had written a melody about a girl he loved, but had kept her name a secret, so that only he and she knew what he had done. And perhaps even she had never known; perhaps it was an enigma known only to himself, a tiny place in his heart kept specially for her.

Cassa turned restlessly, pacing about the room. Had Elgar come into this room too, played his music here? Had the sound of his violin sung its sweet, piercing song between these walls? Had it laughed and sobbed under the tender strokes of his bow, had its longing risen in a crescendo of yearning, reached a peak of throbbing sound, so that passers-by in the street below would pause to listen in wonder, and even the roosting birds fall silent?

And if it had was it love that had guided him, love for a girl who sat at the window and gazed out across the plain, listening?

There was an answer, perhaps, in the box of letters that her father had discovered in the attic. The box that had been put away so carefully in his study to await his return from Australia. Cassa remembered the look on his face, the trembling excitement in his hands as he lifted out a few, looking at the handwriting—handwriting she had seen that very day in the cottage at Broadheath. He had wanted to read them at once but there had been no time. And Cassa, longing to read them too, had taken them firmly and put them away again, closing the lid.

'It's all right, Dad,' she'd said. 'I won't look at them. I'll keep them carefully and you shall be the first to read them. In any case—I'm not sure I want to know. I like secrets to remain secrets. I like the mystery of the *Enigma*.'

But now she wanted to know. She wanted to know if the girl, now long dead, had felt the pain she was feeling now. She wanted to know if she had indeed loved a man who was not for her, and how she had endured her loss.

Across the years, there was a bond between them. And that long-ago pain might help Cassa to bear her own now. That bond could be all she had to hold on to.

She wandered into the study. The box had been placed in a cupboard, locked in case of intruders. Cassa had the key on her own key-ring. She took it out and looked at it.

She would be breaking a trust with her father if she opened that box. Yet if he were here she knew that he would have supported her. She knew that he would not have wanted her to keep any promise that meant pain for her.

All the same. . . She looked at the key again. Put it back in her pocket. Turned away, walked to the door. Walked back again, looked at the cupboard, took out the key. And fitted it into the lock.

It turned as if with its own strength, and the door opened. Cassa reached inside like a sleepwalker and took out the box.

It wasn't a large box. It held perhaps two dozen or so letters, their envelopes yellowed and brittle, tied in two bundles with ribbon that must once have been coloured but was now grey with age. Cassa took them out and laid them on the table, then sat in her father's chair and stared at them.

How Jet would love to be here now! she thought. He wanted so badly to see those letters. New, unseen material happened so rarely in a biographer's life. She remembered hearing about some hitherto unknown letters from Wordsworth to his wife that had been found only a few years ago, and how they had changed everyone's ideas about the poet's marriage. Gold to the biographer who had been the first to use them. And Jet hoped for the same vein of riches to be tapped in these letters, the same kind of revelation.

She reached out and touched the bundles, reluctant even now to untie the ribbons and open the first envelope. Someone had treasured these letters; someone had tied them up, kept them safe in this little box. Had that someone looked ahead down the years and thought of a girl sitting here on a warm early-summer evening, lonely and sad? Had that someone ever thought that these letters and whatever story they told might form a bond across the years?

Of course she hadn't. She'd never intended that anyone should read them—she'd kept them for herself, because she couldn't bear to get rid of them. And even now, somewhere, her ghost might be stirring uneasily at the thought of her secret being a secret no longer.

Cassa looked up nervously, almost as if she expected to see the girl's shadow before her, pointing an accusing finger. She got up quickly, leaving the letters on the table, and went to the window. For a moment she half believed herself to be back in a former century. She looked down into the road, thankful to see a normal twentieth-century car go by, and a couple of girls, jean-clad and giggling.

And then she stiffened slightly. It was almost fully dark now, the street lit by a tall lamp. Surely there had been someone standing under that lamp a moment ago, someone who had moved into the shadows of the bushes that surrounded the gateway? Was someone watching the house?

She felt a tingle of unease. She was alone in the house; there was nobody within call. How many people knew that her parents were away? It was no secret in Malvern. And, although there was little of any great value in the house, there were certain pictures, certain family heirlooms that could be worth enough to make a burglary a good night's work to some petty crook. She stepped back from the window, wondering who was there and whether he could see her.

The shadow moved. So there had been someone! A tall figure detached itself from the darker shadow of the trees and stood in the gateway, its head lifted as if looking up at the windows of her flat. Cassa's heart jumped and beat unevenly.

Who would want to watch her flat? And why?

And then he moved again and something familiar in the movement caught at her memory. She had seen that gesture before, that tilting of the head, that half attentive, half mocking, quizzical inclination. . .

Jet Tayler.

Jet Tayler was watching her house, her flat.

She drew back further into the room, suddenly desperately anxious that he should not see her. Her heart was thudding in her throat now. What was he doing there? Why was he staring at her window?

Did he know, by some strange telepathy, that she was thinking about the letters, that she had actually come to the brink of reading them? Was he so anxious—so *determined*—to see them that he had come here tonight to try yet again to persuade her? Was that all he had been thinking about, all the time?

She thought about the times they had met, the interest he had shown in her, his words about friendship. He didn't want a commitment—no, that would be difficult to extricate himself from later—but friendship, yes, the kind of friendship that would make it impossible for her to refuse his so-reasonable request. And he tried to take that friendship further, too. She remembered his kisses on the hill and in the meadow, and her blush rose, even though she was alone, as she recalled her own response to him. She'd wanted them, invited them—there was no denying that. Her lips had parted to meet his, her body had strained towards him, she'd shivered with delight at his caress. Her heart had leapt under his hand, and she'd moved against him, inviting him to touch her, wanting his body against hers, wanting more, wanting him. . .

Had he thought, even then, of the letters? Had he thought that they could enjoy a light summer affair, soon over, a frothy flirtation that signified nothing— but would have meant, along with her physical capitulation, that she would be willing to let him see the letters? Had that been all that was in his mind?

Her heart cold and heavy in her breast, Cassa knew that the answer had to be yes. Jet had no personal interest in her. He was a man, no less likely than the next man to take what was freely offered, but first in his mind, taking priority all the time, had been his work. The biography he was so keen to write. The way he earned his living.

He was a man of great charm, she acknowledged miserably, a magnetic personality who had set a trap perhaps without even knowing it. And she had fallen into that trap—and into love with him.

She had done what she had sworn she would never do again. Once again, even though warned by the dark green stone, the jasper she had picked up only that morning, she had courted the rejection that she feared most.

Jet's shadow moved again, turned away and disappeared along the road. Cassa watched him go with a bleakness in her heart. Whatever he had come for, whether or not he had thought to try again to persuade her, he had evidently thought better of it. And she felt as if she had been abandoned.

Knowing that her feelings were totally irrational, yet knowing also that the pain of them was none the less for that, she picked up the box and put it back in the cupboard. She locked the door and went out of the study, checked that everything was as it should be in the rest of her parents' apartment, then went back to her own flat. Without putting on the lights, she walked across to the window and looked down again at the road.

There was no tall shadow there now. Across the plain, the fields and woods had been swallowed by the darkness, and low in the sky she saw a full moon, hazy with the mist of the evening over the river, yellow with the after-glow of sunset.

She would not look at the letters—not tonight, at any rate. She had a strange, almost superstitious feeling that Jet Tayler could look into her mind; that if she read the letters he would know, that he would even be able to divine their secrets. She could not take the risk.

And she knew now that she had more to think about than the letters, or even Jet. She was reaching the point where she must face what had happened in her own life. Where she must take out her own memories and look at them, and admit at last why the dark green jasper figured so largely in her life. Why the stone of rejection came so readily into her hand.

CHAPTER FIVE

AFTER a sleepless night Cassa found herself in the tiny kitchen, dressed in a long T-shirt with a picture of Mickey Mouse on the front—which was her substitute for a dressing-gown—and staring at a piece of toast she had no recollection of making.

Mechanically, she laid it on a plate and spread it with butter. She carried it into the sitting-room with a mug of coffee and sat down by the window, looking down at the trees which clustered by the gateway and remembering Jet Tayler's tall shadow, looming taller than ever in the moonlight as he'd stood gazing up at her window the night before. The memory brought a shiver brushing across her skin, and she rubbed her bare arms as if to dispel an actual touch.

What had he been doing there? What had he been thinking of? Was he wondering how to get into the house, how to obtain the letters he wanted so badly to read? And had every move he had made, every overture of friendliness—and more then friendliness, she thought, remembering the passion of the kisses they had shared, his passion and her response—been merely a step in his pursuit of the letters?

Had it all been a pretence, his talk of friendship? Was he no more than a callous cynic, making her fall in love with him just so that he could——?

Cassa's whole body jerked, and some of the coffee spilled from the mug she held in her hands. *Fall in love with him*? Was that really what had happened to her?

Had she really been so naïve, so gullible, as to let another man catch her heart? Hadn't she learnt *anything*. . .?

Turning her mind away from him, she found herself thinking once more of the letters, and the girl who had perhaps sat at this very window to read them and write her replies. What had her feelings been? Had she been tremulous, hopeful, dreaming dreams of a future in which there was always music, always love? Or had she felt the breaking of a heart that knew its love could never be fulfilled?

Had she known, even at the start, that her love was hopeless?

Restlessly, Cassa stood up. She crossed the room to her music centre and took out a disc at random. Slotting it in, she switched it on and went back to the window, gazing out. Music had always been a solace. Maybe now it would fill her mind and heart, blotting out the disturbed feelings she was experiencing now, bringing her peace.

And then the music filled the room and she recognised the rich, melodic strains of Elgar's *Enigma Variations*. Of all the pieces to choose! With a muttered exclamation, she wheeled and went back to the player, but even as she stretched out a hand towards it the doorbell rang. For a moment she hesitated—she didn't have to answer it, did she? But before she could make up her mind it was followed by a tap on the door. Whoever it was knew her and knew the routine: ring the bell at the top of the outside steps, then come straight up to knock on the door to the flat. That was if Cassa didn't already have it open, waiting.

Cassa shrugged and went to the door. At least it might take her mind of other things to have someone to talk to. Though it was oddly early for callers. . . She paused again, wondering with a sudden lurch of her heart if it might be Jet. But the figure seen dimly through the glass was short, too short and stocky for Jet. Reassured, she opened the door—and gasped.

'Hello, Cassandra,' James Meakin said, smiling like a benign owl on the little landing. 'I hope you don't mind our coming so early, but we wanted to catch you before you left for the shop. Jet wants particularly to get things settled as soon as possible. He's anxious to start work—I'm sure you'll understand that.'

Cassa looked past him at the tall figure which had been out of sight from the door, standing at the top of the stairs just round the corner. Jet Tayler returned her gaze steadily, then his eyes travelled downwards, taking in her slender body in the T-shirt that came barely halfway down her thighs, and his lips twitched.

Cassa felt her face flame. For a moment she felt like slamming the door in their faces—but that would have been unpardonably rude to her father's best and oldest friend. Silently, she stood aside so that they could come in. She half turned towards the bedroom, intending to put on something that would cover her more adequately, but an imp of defiance entered her heart. Why should she do anything of the sort? Why shouldn't she dress as she wanted in her own home? She hadn't asked him to come calling at this hour.

James Meakin walked into the sitting-room with the easy familiarity of someone who had been so long a friend of the family that he was almost part of it. Jet followed with not much less confidence. He glanced down at Cassa as he passed her, and she met his eyes briefly before looking down again at the floor. Her heart was thumping rapidly, and she didn't want him to notice her quickened breathing.

Was it only yesterday that he had taken her out, to Broadheath, to see Elgar's birthplace and have a picnic in a nearby meadow? Was it less than twenty-four hours ago that she had lain in his arms in the grass, feeling his lips on hers, returning his kiss with a passion she had scarcely known herself capable of? That she had been ready to give herself to him, lost to all thought, all sensation but her need of him, of the fiery desires his fingertips were waking on her skin and in her body? That her heart had been beating to the music of love. . .?

But it had been nothing but a dream, she reminded herself fiercely. Only moments later they'd had that talk about commitment and she'd known without doubt that Jet, a true Aquarius after all, was not and never would be ready to make that commitment. And, to salvage just a few shreds of pride, she had denied that there was anything more than a casual pleasure for her, either, in the kisses they had shared.

What else could she have done?

So what was Jet doing here now? she wondered as she followed the two men into her own sitting-room. And why was James with him—and what was all this talk about wanting to 'get things settled'? Surely he hadn't asked James to intercede over the letters? Had he *still* not accepted the fact that she just wasn't going to go against her father's wishes and show them to him?

Perhaps he had actually gone as far as getting James to telephone her father in Australia? But if that had been the case surely Dad would have simply rung Cassa himself? He wouldn't have sent James to persuade her. . .

'It's all right,' Jet said suddenly, and his voice was oddly gentle, though there was a tinge of amusement in it as well, 'we haven't come to evict you—don't look so frightened.'

'I'm not looking frightened!' Cassa flashed at once, and he smiled. Feeling unreasonably annoyed, she turned her back on him and went to turn off the music. It was altogether too appropriate. She spoke directly to James, who had settled himself in an armchair as if he were in his own home. 'I'm sorry, James, but I don't have much time—as you say, I have to get to the shop. Suky said she might be late this morning. So if you'd just tell me what this is all about——'

'Of course, my dear.' James spoke peaceably, with the unhurried air of someone who had never had to be anywhere early in the morning. 'It's really quite simple. As you know, Jet's been staying with me while he looks around Malvern and the area, gathering material for his biography. Now, the other evening while we were talking——'

'You told him about the letters,' Cassa interrupted. 'Yes, we've been through all that and I've told him Dad doesn't want them to be read until he can come home and do it himself. And, since they've been there for nearly a hundred years, I can't really see that a few more weeks——'

'Please, my dear.' James held up a thin, almost white hand. 'You're running ahead of yourself. I did tell Jet about the letters, yes, but it isn't just that. I happened to be speaking to your father on the telephone last night and——'

'So you *have* spoken to him!' Cassa stared at him,

then turned to Jet. 'You went behind my back,' she accused him. 'You got James to talk to Dad and persuade him, and now you've come here to—to gloat over me. I suppose you want them straight away—you can't wait to take them away and find out——'

'Cassandra, *please*!' Once again James stopped her. His voice, thin with age, caught at her as Jet's deep, vibrant tones could never have done at that moment. She paused, biting her lip, feeling the tears sting her eyes. She had never been so rude to her father's friend before and she felt a deep blush of shame flood into her face.

'I'm sorry, James,' she said quietly after a moment. 'I was just. . . Please go on.'

James smiled at her then with such understanding that she wanted to cry. Yet could it be true understanding? Could he really know what was going on in her mind, in her heart? Could anyone?

'I didn't telephone your father about Jet,' he said. 'It was to do with an old student of his and mine—a young woman who had gone to settle in Australia. I'd been trying to track down her address so that he could visit her, and yesterday I obtained it. But while we were talking I mentioned Jet and what he was doing, and he——'

'Said I could show him the letters,' Cassa said drearily. 'Well, it comes to the same thing, doesn't it?'

'Not at all,' James said kindly. 'The letters weren't mentioned, in fact. I just happened to say that Jet was staying here for a while and was looking for somewhere to stay while he works on the biography. And your father suggested that he should use the attic flat here.'

Cassa lifted her head and stared at him.

'The *attic* flat?' She looked up at the ceiling. '*This* attic flat—in this house? But——'

'Certainly. And it struck me as being a very good idea. I've never been happy about your being alone in this house while your parents were away. The thought that Jet's here will be a great relief to me, and your father agrees——'

'But Dad doesn't even *know* Jet!'

'Not well, certainly, but they've met at university functions and he remembers him. In any case, he trusts my judgement.' The reproof was mild but unmistakable, and Cassa coloured again. 'Anyway, it really is up to your father who occupies the attic flat. Presumably you wouldn't have expected the right to vet any other applicant.'

'No, of course not,' Cassa muttered, feeling she had been out-manoeuvred.

There was a tiny silence, then James said, 'You must say, of course, if you're really unhappy about this arrangement, Cassa. But, I must admit, I thought—well, the two of you seemed to be getting on so well. Jet tells me you spent the day together yesterday. It never occurred to me that you'd be anything other than pleased, but—Jet can easily look for somewhere else if you——'

'No, it's all right.' Cassa spoke quickly, nervously, unable to bear any more of James's perplexity. 'Of course I have no objection.' If only that were true! But she could find no words to voice the objection she had, and she would never have been able to tell James anyway—not about those kisses that had set her heart racing, the caresses that had brought fire to her skin, the overwhelming desire that had brought her to helplessness in Jet's arms. And, in any case, surely forewarned was forearmed—now that she knew the effect

Jet could have on her, couldn't she make quite sure that it never happened again? Once again she was uncomfortably aware of her skimpy T-shirt. 'The flats are quite self-contained,' she went on, speaking too quickly but unable to slow down her rapid tones. 'We need hardly see each other—I mean——'

'Cassa means she doesn't approve of neighbours who are forever popping in to borrow a cup of sugar,' Jet interrupted, a quiver of amusement in his deep voice. 'And she's quite right, of course.' He sketched her a quick mock-bow. 'I promise to come fully equipped with sugar, eggs and everything else the prudent flat-dweller should have. Or is it instant coffee that's so important these days? Isn't that the modern excuse for getting to know each other?'

Cassa glanced at him and then away, half amused and half irritated by the bright laughter in his eyes. 'We know each other quite well enough,' she said crossly. 'There's no need for coffee, or——' Oh, what was she saying? He'd got her into such a state that she was talking nonsense. Well, he needn't think she was going to be available for teasing just because he lived in the flat upstairs. She would make it quite clear from the start that they might as well be living at opposite ends of the country. Indeed, she would do her best to ensure that she saw just about as much of him as if they were. . . 'I suppose you want the keys,' she said, and went to the small bureau in the corner. 'And then I'll have to ask you to go, I'm afraid. I really do have to go out soon. And, as you see——' she glanced down at herself '—I'm not anywhere near ready.'

'Really?' There was no mistaking amusement in Jet's voice now. 'I thought it was quite the fashion to go out in a Mickey Mouse T-shirt and not much else.' His voice lingered a little over the words. 'I assume there's not much else, anyway.'

Cassa felt as if her face would never stop burning. If only she'd gone to find something else to put on, as her first instincts had suggested! Why had she been so deliberately provocative? Well, she certainly wouldn't be making *that* mistake again—not if he were to be living here. She wouldn't answer the door again without first wrapping herself up in everything short of scarf and gloves. And she might even consider them.

'Here are the keys,' she said stiffly, holding them out. 'I'm afraid I don't have time to come up and show you round, but I think everything's self-explanatory anyway. If there's anything you don't understand I'll be home soon after five, or you could call at the shop.' She hesitated. 'I don't think there's anything else, is there?'

'In other words, James, we're being dismissed,' Jet said, smiling, and Cassa felt a quick pang of irritation. Patronising chauvinist! She felt his fingers brush hers as he took the keys, and drew her hand back quickly. And saw from the expression in his eyes that he knew just why she'd done it.

'Yes, I'm afraid you are,' she said, trying for James's benefit to keep her voice light. 'I'm not like you—I have a business to run and customers to attend to.'

'Of course. I'm sure there's a queue already forming of people anxious to buy their day's supply of crystals.' His voice was deadpan, and then he laughed. 'Don't take it all so seriously, Cassa! Life's to be enjoyed— have you forgotten that? You look as if the end of the world is nigh—and you in a Mickey Mouse T-shirt and all!'

If she coloured any more this morning he'd he

thinking it was a suntan, she thought as she felt her skin warm yet again. And as she met his eyes she felt, despite her exasperation, a grin begin to tug at her lips. Oh, bother the man! Why was it that, even when she was most annoyed with him, he still seemed to be able to make her smile. She didn't *want* to smile! She didn't want to laugh. She just wanted him to—to *go*.

'Of course I know life's to be enjoyed,' she said crisply. 'And I'll enjoy it a lot more if you'll both just go now and leave me to get dressed and go to work. You've got the keys; you can move into the flat straight away, since Dad seems to be happy about it.' She gave James a look as if to warn him that she'd have more to say about this later, though how she would ever set about taking her father's friend to task she hadn't the faintest idea. And she was pleassed to see that he looked slightly abashed as he got to his feet and made his way to the door.

'Well, that's all settled, then,' he said heartily. 'I'm sure you'll be very comfortable here, Jet. John and his wife made the attic flat charming, and it's more than adequately furnished. Just the place for you to work.'

They went out. Cassa stood at the door as they passed, shrinking back slightly so that Jet would not brush against her. She was once more acutely conscious of the fact that she had very little on—and that Jet knew it. Yet again she felt the betraying colour in her cheeks as she met his eyes, but this time she refused to look away. She held his gaze, defying him to smile, her chin up and her lips pressed firmly together. And it worked. He didn't smile. He just looked gravely back at her, his eyes dark, almost black, with no more than a rim of silver around the widened pupils. For a moment or two he didn't even blink.

But there was something there, she knew. Some emotion, unexpressed. Some reaction to her look, to her nearness.

And it had, surely, to be amusement. What else could it be?

Cassa worked hard in the shop that day, changing the window displays, putting a fresh delivery of crystals into a display case, setting out new books on the shelves, and trying all the time to dispel the memory of Jet's expression from her mind. But she kept coming back to it, to that long, level, darkened gaze; kept seeing it again, feeling the sharp tingle in her stomach, the quick leap of her heart. Kept pushing it away at once, afraid of what it might mean, afraid of what might be happening to her.

'I said, Cassa—what shall we do with the crystal ball? Is it to go back in the window, or do you want something else on that little shelf?'

Cassa brought herself back to the present with a start. Suky was looking at her with puzzled eyes, the crystal ball glowing softly in her hands. 'Is everything all right, Cassa?' she asked anxiously. 'You don't seem to be here this morning.'

'Sorry.' Cassa looked at the crystal ball and wished that she were able to read it. What would it show her? But you should never try to read for yourself, any more than you could read stones for yourself or cast your own horoscope. You needed someone else to do that for you.

Someone else had once read the crystals for her, she remembered, and told her things she hadn't wanted to know. But that was all in the past.

Suky was still gazing at her and she pulled herself

together, trying to remember what the other girl had asked.

'Yes, let's have it in the window. It always attracts interest. And that amethyst necklace near it, I think.' She glanced restlessly around the little shop. 'We need something new in here to brighten things up a bit. I don't know what. . .' A glitter of colour from a prism caught her eye and she stared at it, thinking suddenly, inexplicably, of Jet. 'Rainbows,' she said, half under her breath. 'Midnight rainbows. . .' But the thought was gone, and once again she saw his eyes, that steady gaze, and felt the kick of her heart, the almost unbearable tingle of her stomach. Abruptly, she turned away. 'You do something, Suky. You're good at displays.'

Suky was good at them, but all the same Cassa usually liked to do the window herself. She felt a proprietorial, almost jealous interest in her window display. This morning, however, she hardly cared. What did it matter who did it, after all?

But Suky didn't move. She went on standing there, her eyes fixed on Cassa's face, and there was concern, even anxiety, in them.

'Cassa, are you all right?' she asked again. 'You don't feel ill or anything? I can look after things here if you want to go home. If it's a migraine coming on——'

'I don't get migraines.' Cassa knew she was speaking curtly, but it couldn't be helped. 'I'm quite all right, Suky. Just didn't sleep too well, that's all. You get on with the window; I've got these invoices to sort out. There's a big coach just arrived at the hotel—we might get some customers later on. I'd like to be ready for them.'

Suky gave her a worried look but said nothing more,

and for a while the two girls worked in silence. Cassa concentrated on the invoices, using the paperwork to keep her mind off Jet. But already she was wondering whether she wouldn't have been better to have done the display. Handling the crystals might have been more soothing than wrestling with figures. On the other hand, her own negative emotions might have found their way into the stones and spoiled them for the customers, even tinged the atmosphere in the shop with her uncertainty. It might be better not to have too much to do with them while she was feeling like this. It might be better not to come into the shop at all. . .

With an exclamation she flung down her pen, and Suky, who was leaning into the window to complete her arrangements, looked round in surprise. Cassa shuffled all the invoices together and crammed them into a drawer.

'I'm sorry, Suky. You're right—I'm doing no good here today. I think I'll have to go out—have a walk on the hills or something to clear my head.' She ran her fingers through her short dark hair. 'It's not a headache—I just don't seem able to think, to concentrate. . .'

Suky climbed carefully out of the window and came over to her. 'If there's anything I can do——'

'Just take care of things here, if you don't mind.' Cassa smiled ruefully and apologised again. 'I seem to be taking advantage of you lately—this is the second day running that I've gone off and left you to cope.'

'It's all right. I can manage. I just wish there were more——'

'It's nothing anyone can help me with,' Cassa said slowly, as if the realisation had just come to her. 'It's something I have to sort out for myself. One of those stupid feelings you have to work out of your system—nothing more than that.' She grinned suddenly at her friend's anxious face. 'A good long walk will do it, I'm sure. I'll be in here tomorrow again, right as rain, bossing you about as if nothing had happened.' She laughed. 'What am I saying? Nothing *has* happened! Nothing at all.'

Suky smiled too, but her look was still anxious, and Cassa realised that her own laugh had been brittle, almost forced. She turned away quickly and grabbed her bag. Best to get out before she said any more, before she gave herself away completely.

But what was there to give away? she asked herself as she walked up to the long terrace of shops that looked down over the town. What, but a silly obsession, a disturbance that meant nothing, over a man she scarcely knew? What had happened to her to make her behave like a foolish teenager, acting like a frightened rabbit over nothing?

Crossing the road, she climbed up the ninety-nine steps that led up to the zigzag path to St Ann's Well. It was here that she had met Jet Tayler only yesterday—it seemd an age ago. She climbed rapidly past the well, ignoring the people sitting about in the sun-trap outside drinking coffee, and went up on to the wide, sunny slopes of the Worcester Beacon.

Even here she was haunted by memories of Jet. Up there, in the shadow of the burnt-out café, she had stumbled almost into his arms, had found herself in his embrace, being kissed by him, returning those kisses. . . Her face grew hot at the memory, but she couldn't help lingering over it, recalling each kiss in detail, savouring again the touch of his lips, his tongue, feeling his hands on her body, moving gently, caressingly, calling forth a desire she hadn't known since——

No! No, she wouldn't think of that, wouldn't allow the memories to go on. Wouldn't even let the thought of those other kisses and caresses into her mind at the same time as Jet's. Wouldn't admit, even to herself, the fierce burning pain of that old humiliation. . .

She hadn't thought of it for an age. Why should it keep coming into her mind now?

Cassa walked on, striding steadily along the paths of the hills, passing the beacon, passing the toposcope that had been designed by Elgar's friend Troyte Griffith, one of the subjects of the *Enigma Variations*, passing the low stone seat that pointed the way to the different viewpoints. She walked along the narrow ridge which had once been the boundary of the two counties, looking to her left over the plains of Worcestershire, to her right across the tumbled hills of Herefordshire towards the dark silhouettes of the Black Mountains. She came to the Wyche Cutting, where the road had been driven though the rocks, and crossed to go on, still walking the ridge, her eyes now on the terraced slopes of the ancient hill-fort of Herefordshire Beacon, known locally as British Camp.

How far she intended to walk she had no idea. It was as if she needed to go on and on, to leave behind the memories that haunted her, the thoughts that troubled her. As if she needed to walk until she was too tired to think, too exhausted to remember.

And then? The thought of sleep, rest, oblivion, hung in her mind like a desirable prize. But she knew that it wouldn't be enough. It wouldn't be the answer.

Eventually she would have to wake up, face another day, face the future. Face the present.

Face the past.

Yes, she thought, sitting down suddenly on a wooden seat. That's what all this is about, isn't it? The past. The past I don't want to face, the past I've tried so hard to escape from, to pretend never happened. The past that haunts me still and won't let me get on with my life.

She thought of the stone she had picked up, the green jasper that denoted rejection, the pain it had brought her. And which rejection did it mean—the one she had suffered all those years ago, or the one she was so afraid of now? Because she *was* afraid—she knew that. She was afraid of being rejected again, terribly afraid. Because she had never come to terms with that first time, never got over the pain of it, never put it quite behind her. And now that she was in a position to be rejected. . .

But why shouldn't I be afraid? she argued silently. Jet Tayler has never made any secret of the fact that he doesn't want a commitment. He's gone out of his way to make that clear. And he's an Aquarius—he'll avoid marriage, or any other sort of commitment, for as long as possible. She thought of the feral look in his gleaming eyes, the eagle's face, impressions that were deepened by his hair, gold-brown like the strong, beating wings of a soaring bird of prey. The untameable quality of him, the restless nature that kept him roaming the world.

Jet Tayler was bad news for any girl who might be tempted to fall in love with him. Especially, he was bad news for Cassa.

Falling in love with Jet meant rejection, as the night

followed the day. It wasn't even his fault. All she could do was avoid him.

And how is that possible, she asked herself bitterly, now that he'll be living in the same house? Now that I'll be able to hear him moving about overhead, now that we're likely to meet at any time on the stairs, now that he can come and knock on the door at any hour of the day or night. . .

Impatiently, with more than a touch of desperation, she got up and continued her walk. At least she could keep out of the way while he was moving in. And hope that she could get in through her own door that evening without his seeing or hearing her.

But when she finally returned, as exhausted as she'd hoped she would be, much later that day it was to find someone quite other than Jet Tayler waiting for her at the top of the stairs.

The man was less tall than Jet, and his figure was slight rather than lean. His hair was fair, without the burnished sheen of Jet's and his face did not have the hawk-like arrogance that made Jet's so arresting. His eyes were blue, rather pale, and he was dressed fault-lessly, as if he had stepped off the pages of a fashion magazine, and, whereas Jet looked as if he owned his clothes, this man looked as if his clothes owned him.

But that was to be expected, Cassa thought irrelev-ently as she stopped, half frozen with shock as she stared at him. Fashion was, after all, Gerry Cornewell's business.

'So there you are, Cassa,' he said pleasantly in his light, somewhat edged voice. 'I've been wondering when you might come home. Your lodger upstairs didn't seem to know. He offered to give you a message, but I said I'd rather wait.' He smiled slowly like a

Cheshire cat. 'It's a pity I didn't have a key, as I used to have in London. I could have started to prepare a meal for us both. Or at least a drink.'

Cassa found her voice, but it was barely more than a whisper. Shock was still pounding through her in great pulsating waves. How had Gerry Cornewell come here? *Why* had he come? Today of all days, when she had been trying to face at last the memory of what he had done to her, to come to terms with the memories she'd been trying for so long to repress?

'What are you doing here, Gerry?' she asked in that dry, painful whisper. 'Why have you come back? It's all over—finished—forgotten.'

Gerry smiled again and she wondered how she could ever have thought she loved him, how she could ever have waited, breathless, for that smile.

'Oh, I don't think so, do you? Not forgotten, anyway. And probably not over, either. But why don't we discuss it, inside? Don't you know I'm longing to see this little flat of yours?'

Cassa hesitated. The last thing she wanted was to let Gerry Cornewell into her flat. But neither did she want a scene out here on the landing, with Jet Tayler almost certainly an interested listener up the stairs. Reluctantly, she slid her key into the lock and turned it.

Gerry drifted past her and she followed him in and shut the door.

'Well!' he said in the languid way that was so much his. 'This really is very pleasant indeed. You've certainly used your talents to good effect here, Cassa, my darling. But then, you always were good at making a home, weren't you?' He turned and smiled down at her. 'Do you know, I think it was a very good idea of mine to come and look you up.'

Cassa looked at him stonily.

'Look me up?' she said, and was glad to find that her voice was stronger now. 'Is that all this is, Gerry? Or have you got something else in mind?'

He laughed.

'What a suspicious little mind it has! Now what else *could* I have in mind, Cassa, my sweet? Or are you hoping for something more than a friendly visit?'

'No,' she said. 'I'm not hoping for anything from you, Gerry. And there's nothing here for you, either—nothing. So I suggest that you leave right now. I happen to be rather tired and I want a rest.'

'Rest away,' he said, and his eyes and voice had hardened. 'But I'm not leaving, Cassa—not yet. You and I have some talking to do. And I intend to do it now. This evening. And nothing is going to stop me.'

Cassa stared at him. For the first time she began to feel a little frightened. She cast an involuntary glance upwards, wondering whether to call for Jet. But Gerry saw her look and laughed again.

'The hunky lodger? Afraid not, darling. He's gone out. And your parents are away too, aren't they? So there's no one here but the two of us. You and me.' He came close and touched her chin with one finger, tipping her face up towards his. 'Just like the old days,' he said, and bent to lay his lips on hers.

CHAPTER SIX

CASSA struggled free and backed away, her eyes on Gerry's face. She was definitely scared now—and that was strange, for she'd never felt scared of Gerry before. She'd been angry with him, yes; she'd felt contempt, disgust—and once, long ago, she'd thought herself in love with him. But—scared. . .?

'What do you want with me?' she asked, and heard her voice tremble a little. 'Why have you come here? It's over three years since——'

'Since that little bit of trouble we had? I know.' He was leaning against the door of the sitting-room, trapping her inside, but had made no further attempt to touch her. A small smile played about his lips. 'And I thought it was time we patched up our differences. It all seems very trivial after all this time, doesn't it? So silly to go on being sworn enemies.'

'I'm not your sworn enemy.' She was regaining control now, fighting back that surge of panic. 'I don't feel anything for you at all. And I'm not particularly interested in patching up any differences—it's all forgotten now; it doesn't matter to me any more; I haven't even thought about you for—for a long time.' Her voice was rising again, perhaps because what she was saying just wasn't true. It had been until a week or so ago, she told herself fiercely. But then Jet had come along and woken all sorts of emotions in her, and the memory of Gerry and what he had done had started to intrude again, reminding her of old pains and fears that

113

still froze her heart. She fought to pull herself together, lower her voice, and when she spoke again it was low and husky. 'Please, Gerry, go away. There's nothing for us to say to each other now.'

'On the contrary,' he drawled, coming right into the room and dropping gracefully on to the long couch, 'I think there's a good deal to say. Now, why don't we be civilised about this, Cassa, my sweet? Offer me a drink, why don't you, and let's behave like rational human beings? I'm not going to hurt you.'

No? she thought, passing him at a wary distance to go to the kitchen. You hurt me a lot before. But there was little point in not doing as he suggested, though she'd see to it that he didn't have more than one drink. She poured two glasses of wine and carried them back.

Gerry took his, held it up to the light, sniffed it and then tasted it slowly, while Cassa watched with irritation. He'd always done this, she remembered, showing off his knowledge of wines. In a moment he would pronounce on this one. 'An unpretentious little wine,' he would probably say. 'Nice, light bouquet, pleasant enough for everyday drinking. Probably from the vineyards of. . .' But, for once, he said nothing, merely sipped and then put the glass on the low table beside the couch.

Cassa sat down slowly on the edge of one of the armchairs, facing him. She was still wondering why he had come. It was no casual visit, she was sure of that. Nor had he come out of a desire to put right what had happened nearly four years ago. Gerry wasn't the sort to harbour a guilty conscience.

Cassa's mind went back to the days when she had believed herself in love with the man who sat opposite her now. How had he managed to enslave her as he had? she wondered. How had it come about that she had idolised him, been ready to follow him anywhere, thought herself the most privileged of girls to be seen in his company?

Why, she'd actually been pleased—*thrilled*—the first time she'd seen herself pictured with him in one of the leading gossip columns. 'Dress designer Gerry Cornewell, escorting his latest beauty Cassandra Newton to his spring show,' the caption had run, and added a coy, 'Did petite, dark-haired Cassie inspire his latest line in wedding dresses?'

She hadn't liked the diminutive of her name that the newspaper had used, but the implication that Gerry might be taking her more seriously than any of her forerunners had been deliciously exciting, and she'd kept the newspaper clipping for a long time. Until the day when she'd thrown out all such reminders of her folly, the day when she'd seen Gerry for what he was. The day when she'd suffered a rejection so humiliating that it could still make her heart shrink away from love. . .

She'd met Gerry in London, where she'd been studying textile design and working as part of her course in one of the most famous London stores. She'd loved it, handling the beautiful rich fabrics all day, helping to swathe them around the dummies for window displays, draping great swatches like curtains across the back of the windows to set off the vibrant arrangements. There had been the interest of working with the customers too, helping them choose the best materials for the patterns they wanted to use, even helping them choose the patterns that would best suit their own figures and styles. The store she worked in had prided itself on doing more than merely hand over goods in exchange for money, and Cassa had loved the feeling that somewhere in London there were women wearing styles she had helped them choose, in fabrics she had recommended.

At other times she had found herself working for short periods with different designers—never in the inner sanctum, of course, never as much more than a kind of dogsbody, but nevertheless soaking up the atmosphere of a busy fashion house and learning, learning all the time. And that was how she had come to meet Gerry Cornewell.

She knew about him, of course, before she went to his workrooms. Everyone knew about Gerry Cornewell, the latest bright star in the fashion firmament, tipped to take over where the Emanuels left off. His clothes were attracting interest everywhere, especially since at least one royal duchess had been seen in his creations. And Gerry himself was as colourful as his clothes—always being seen in the most exclusive night-spots, sauntering through the Royal Enclosure at Ascot, on the riverbank at Henley, eating strawberries and cream at Wimbledon. And never without a beautiful woman by his side.

Cassa had never expected him to notice her, a skinny student barely out of her teens, doing the most menial of tasks in his workrooms. In fact, the first time he came in when she was there she was sorting buttons—hundreds of them, it seemed, looking for a particular type which would go well with a new autumn suit. She'd been doing it half the day and was beginning to see buttons before her eyes whenever she glanced up for a moment. When Gerry Cornewell stopped in front of her she didn't even realise who he was; just felt a weary irritation because he was standing in her light.

'Sorry, was there something you wanted?' she asked, barely glancing at him, resigning herself to being sent on yet another task before she'd completed the one in hand.

'I'm not sure.' The drawling voice was one she hadn't heard before and she did look up then, shading her tired eyes with one hand. Because he was standing against the bright, harsh light that shone down from the ceiling she still couldn't see his face, but she registered the slender, graceful figure and knew at once, from newspaper and magazine photographs, who this must be. Hastily, her face flaming with embarrassment, she jumped up and, catching the edge of the big table with her knee, sent hundreds of buttons flying all over the floor.

'Oh, *no*!'

Cassa stared in dismay at the scattered mosaic of buttons. It had taken her hours to sort them all out, and now she'd have to do it all over again. And for this to happen in front of Gerry Cornewell, of all people. . . She saw her career fading in front of her eyes, beginning with her dismissal from the Cornewell workrooms and expulsion from her course.

But Gerry Cornewell didn't seem to be at all put out. As Cassa's boss hurried over to see what had happened, he merely laughed and shook his head. His eyes were on Cassa all the time as he claimed entire responsibility for the accident.

'All my fault, Zelda! I startled this young lady—she was so absorbed in her work that she didn't even hear me coming. Look, let's scoop them all up into a box—they can be sorted again another day.'

'But we were looking for a button to go on the new

Winterleaf collection——' Zelda began, but again he shook his head.

'No need. I found just the thing this morning. Now, where's a box? Ah, yes, that one will do. Just jumble them all in—that's it.' He smiled at Cassa and her heart turned over. 'You know, you look as if you've done enough for today,' he said authoritatively. 'I'm going to carry you away for a cup of tea. That's all right, isn't it, Zelda—you don't need this delightful young person any more this afternoon, do you?'

It clearly wasn't all right with Zelda, who had had several other tasks in mind for Cassa to do before she was allowed to go home, but she didn't say so. Instead, tight-lipped, she shovelled all the buttons into the box and turned away. And Cassa was too young, too inexperienced and too bemused to realise that she could be storing up trouble for herself. Or to realise just what was really going on that afternoon—what Gerry Cornewell's attention really signified.

Looking at him now, in the peace of her own flat, Cassa wondered how she could ever have been so naïve.

Gerry looked across at her and smiled. It was the same smile that had enraptured her that afternoon in the big London workroom. But it no longer had the effect of turning her heart over. Instead, it left her quite cold.

'What do you want, Gerry?' she asked again. 'Why have you come here?'

'Why, to see you again, my sweet. Didn't I say so?' He picked up his glass again, twirled it a little, drank and set it down again. His eyes met hers. 'We had some good times together, didn't we?'

Cassa didn't answer. It was true that Gerry had

taken her to all the right places, shown her the most glamorous side of London life. True that he'd insisted she should dress like a model, in the style that would be expected of Gerry Cornewell's. . .what? Girlfriend? Lover? *Mistress*? Her face burned as she thought of how it must have appeared to others, and again she asked herself that question—how, even at twenty years old, could she have been so naïve?

How could she ever have believed that his interest in her had been genuine?

But that was just what she had believed at the time. From that first afternoon, when he'd taken her to tea— not at the local café, where she usually went, but at the Ritz, no less!—Cassa had been bowled over, totally overwhelmed by his dazzling attentions. Nothing she had experienced before had prepared her for this. Flowers arriving, chocolates, champagne—her flat-mate in the rather down-at-heel back-street terraced house had nearly fainted one afternoon when the gifts had begun to arrive—trips to the theatre, to the Café Royal, even Annabel's. . . It was no wonder that she'd had no time even to work out what was happening. Trying to keep up with her course as well had been all she could cope with.

'Didn't we?' he repeated. 'We had some good times. I always enjoyed being with you, Cassa. You were different from the others—young, appealing. Refreshing. I've often thought of those times.'

She watched him drink. He was making the glass of wine last a long time. Perhaps he realised that she wouldn't give him any more, that she expected him to go as soon as he had finished. But as he settled back on the couch she knew that it wasn't going to be so

easy to make him go. Gerry had come here for a
definite purpose.

And she felt a prickle of unease. Not quite the fear
she'd felt before, but still. . .

She wished Jet were in the flat upstairs, and, even in
that moment, appreciated the irony. Only that morning
she'd been totally against his moving in—now she was
longing for his protection. For *Jet's* protection!

Jet's protection, she thought. And yet. . .hadn't she
seen him, too, as a threat?

Gerry was speaking again and she turned her
thoughts back to him. He was talking about the few
months—no more than a few weeks, really—when he
had paid such lavish court to her. When he had dazzled
her with his attention, when she'd really believed that
the world was her oyster, that the glamorous life he
showed her was the only way to live. When she'd lost
her way in his arms, when she'd dreamed through his
kisses, believing that he loved her, believing that she
loved him. . .

'My Winterleaf girl,' he'd murmured, holding her
one night as they gazed out from his penthouse apartment at the lights of London. 'Do you know, that's
what first drew me to you that day in the workroom?
Your lovely dark hair, bent over that table of buttons. . .' He lifted the long black hair into two wings,
holding them over her cheeks. 'You seemed to be the
essence of my new collection,' he whispered. 'You
made me think even then of sharp autumn days in the
woods, frosty mornings on windswept hills.
Winterleaf. . . It's you, Cassa; you.'

She gazed back into his eyes, her heart thumping.
Nothing like this had ever happened to her before.
They'd been drinking champagne and her head was

reeling a little, her mind spinning with the exhilaration of it, with the height and the view across midnight London, with Gerry's nearness and the soft seductiveness of his voice. She could feel his arms, close around her, his hands moving gently over her back, his lips brushing her skin. She closed her eyes, trembling. Was this the moment? Was this the night when they would become lovers? Was this the beginning of the rest of her life?

And then, even as she let her lips part for his kiss, she heard the door open. Light streamed into the flat from the hallway, and a harsh, angry voice split the air.

'So it's true! All the gossip, the rumours—it *is* this little bitch you've been seeing! And I thought it was no more than spite. . .'

Cassa jumped violently, automatically springing away from Gerry, but to her surprise he kept his arms around her, holding her firmly against his side. He turned so that they were both facing the door, and Cassa's heart sank as she recognised Zelda Crane, the head of Gerry's workroom.

'Zelda,' he said, as smoothly as if she had just dropped in for coffee. 'What a pleasant surprise. And so late, too. Whatever brings you here at this hour? And how did you manage to get in?'

'How do you think?' the other woman said through her teeth. 'With my key, of course—the key you gave me when *we* were lovers. They key I suppose you'll want back now, to give to this little slut!'

The venom in her voice made Cassa cringe, but Gerry merely smiled. He didn't show the least trace of surprise. It was almost as if he had planned the whole scene—and, much later, Cassa was to remember that impression and shiver.

'And what if I do?' he asked Zelda. 'You weren't so keen on using your key a few weeks ago, when that so-called film star took your eye. Happy enough to go off and hit LA with him, weren't you? Leave of absence to look after your sick mother—wasn't that the story? But I have my spies, you see—I knew exactly where you were and exactly what you were doing. So you can't blame me if meanwhile I have a little fun on my own account.'

Cassa turned and stared up at him. A little fun? Was that all she'd been to him? Had he been merely using her, while Zelda was away, to amuse himself?

What about all those things he'd said? The things he'd done? Calling her his Winterleaf girl, sending her flowers and chocolates, buying her champagne and exotic, fabulous dinners, taking her out? Had none of it meant a thing?

She couldn't believe it. And neither, apparently, could Zelda.

'A little fun?' she asked, curling her lip. 'Is that what you call it? Getting yourself featured in gossip columns with a child barely out of her cradle? Have you *seen* what the tabloids have been saying about the pair of you?'

She thrust a sheaf of newspapers under their noses, and Cassa felt sick as she recognised some of the most salacious papers and magazines on the market. She had never even thought to look at them. What *had* they been saying?

But Gerry laughed and brushed them aside.

'What does it matter what they say? No publicity is bad publicity, Zelda, darling; you know that. And at least it's brought you running back to me, hasn't it?' He paused, his eyes smiling into those of the woman

who had been his lover for so many years, who had
managed his workroom with such efficiency and then
had stunned him by taking up with a Hollywood film
actor—at just about the time, Cassa realised now, that
he had first noticed her in the workroom and taken her
to tea at the Ritz. There had been talk about Zelda
and the film star then, whispered and giggled about
among the other girls, but Cassa had been too new,
too shy to involve herself with it. And since then she'd
been back at the store, helping customers to choose
patterns and fabric, or in college again, and hadn't
even realised that Zelda had vanished.

'And is that why you did it?' The harshness had
disappeared from Zelda's voice but there was a thread
of menace, of jealousy, still running through it, and
Gerry laughed.

'Well, of course it was, my sweet! You don't imagine
I could be really serious about a chit like this, delightful
as she is?' He drew Zelda to him, while still keeping
one arm around Cassa's waist. 'I don't have time to
initiate little girls,' he murmured. 'Give me a woman
of experience any day—or night.'

Cassa stayed frozen against him for a split second,
then jumped away. She faced them both, trembling
violently. Zelda was held close against Gerry's side
now, and making no effort to detach herself. She
looked smug, complacent. And he. . . He looked as
triumphant as if he had just pulled off the greatest coup
in history.

It had all been planned, Cassa realised. He had
taken her up and made much of her, well aware that in
her naïveté she would detect no hidden purpose in his
behaviour. He had taken her about, lent her clothes
from his collection, made sure they'd be seen. Made

sure they'd be photographed and featured in gossip columns, so that the news of their relationship—so open to conjecture, she realised now with a sickening lurch of the heart—would reach Zelda in Los Angeles. So that Zelda would come back to him.

'Did petite dark-haired Cassie inspire his latest line in wedding dresses?' The caption thudded through her brain as she stared at them both. And she looked down at her dress—a dress from the Winterleaf collection— and wanted to tear it off and throw it in his face. But she couldn't even do that. She had to get home—and she couldn't go out in the skimpy lace undies that were all she wore underneath the dress.

'Is it true?' she asked, a quiver in her voice. 'Is it true, Gerry? Were you just using me to make Zelda jealous?'

He laughed again, but there was an edge of discomfort in his laughter.

'What do you have to complain about, my sweet? You've had a good time, haven't you? I doubt if you'd ever dreamed of going to half the places we've been to, doing half the things we've done together. You must have known it wouldn't last. Be honest, now—weren't you using me just as much as I used you?'

Cassa looked at him. And saw, in that moment, not the glamorous, urbane dress designer with the world at his feet, but a rather commonplace man, dressed up like a male model to hide his shortcomings, using deceit and subterfuge to keep his place in a world that was glittery and unreal. And she had been dragged into it! A hot shame flooded over her as she turned and ran from the apartment. It burned her as she found a taxi outside and went back to her tiny back-street flat. It scorched her throughout the rest of that endless night as she tossed in her narrow bed.

The next morning she packed up the Winterleaf dress and sent it back to Gerry's workroom. She went to the college and told the principal that she had decided to abandon her course, refusing to say why. And she went home to Malvern.

She never told anyone just why she had left, and she was thankful to find that neither her parents nor any of her friends had seen those reports in the gossip columns, linking her name with Gerry's. But the shame of it stayed with her for a long time. And the humiliation of her rejection burned itself like a brand into her heart.

Never again would she allow a man to do that to her.

'If only you'd let me explain,' he was saying now, and Cassa brought herself once more back to the present. 'But you just took off, didn't you? Sent back the dress, left college and disappeared. Do you know, I've had the most dreadful time, trying to track you down. . .? And all so unnecessary. I could have cleared the whole thing up with just a few words.'

'Could you?' she asked sceptically. 'Words I would have understood?'

'Now, don't be catty, darling, it doesn't suit you.' His glass was nearly empty and he glanced at it and then at her. Cassa met his eyes blandly, refusing to rise to the bait. If he wanted another drink let him go out and buy one. There are plenty of pubs around Malvern.

The thought of Gerry in a humble pub nearly made her laugh. A hotel lounge, yes; a nightclub—even a wine bar. But a pub. . .!

'So how would you have cleared it all up?' she asked.

'I had the definite impression that it was Zelda you really wanted, and you didn't do much to dispel that impression. How exactly would you have managed that?'

Gerry laughed. 'Now, Cassa, it's nearly four years ago. You're older now, more sophisticated.' He glanced around the flat. 'I can see how far you've come since those days—why, you were no more than a babe then. And that's just how I treated you—as a lovely child. That's what you were to me, don't you see? It was a delight to take you about, show you life, give you little presents. But it never meant any more than that.' He smiled charmingly. 'My mistake was in not seeing that you didn't realise it. I thought you understood—I had no idea that you might be taking it seriously. It just never occurred to me that you might actually fall in love with me.'

Cassa stared at him. He spoke so glibly that she could have sworn he actually believed what he was saying. But he was right—she *was* more sophisticated now. And she knew that Gerry had been quite well aware of what he was doing, all along the line. He'd used her with a callous disregard for her youth, her naïveté. Indeed, without them he could never have used her so successfully.

'Why don't you just get out, Gerry?' she suggested. 'Like now, this minute. I find I can't actually stand being in the same room as you.'

Gerry's eyes widened. He looked back at her, his face the picture of injured innocence.

'But Cassa, my sweet——'

'And don't call me your "sweet". I'm not your *anything*. Just go.'

'Darling, I don't think you quite understand——'

'No,' Cassa said, getting up and walking over to the door, 'it's you who doesn't understand. Whatever happened between us, Gerry, happened a long time ago. It's over. Finished. Done with. And I don't want to be reminded of it. So—if you'll please do as I ask, and just go. . .'

But Gerry didn't move. Instead, he settled back a little deeper into the cushions of the sofa and tilted his head to smile up at her. And the smile had lost its boyishness and taken on a kind of menace.

'Sorry, Cassa. No can do. You see, I didn't come here just to reminisce over old times, delightful though that would have been. I actually came to ask a favour of you. No, not quite a favour. Repayment of a debt, really. Look, why don't you sit down again so that we can talk about it?'

Cassa looked at him. She saw the face that had been handsome, now beginning to look dissipated, with a pallor that spoke of unhealthy living: too many nightclubs, too much drinking. She saw the slender body, once so willowy, now thin and almost emaciated. She saw a tremor in the languid hands.

All that came from the world Gerry lived in, the world he had made his own. Oh, she had no doubt that you could live in that world and stay healthy, stay sane, but it was all too easy to lose control, to sink into a life of social unreality. All too easy to think that champagne was the only drink, nightclubs the only places to be. And if she had stayed with Gerry she could have been dragged into that world too. She could have lost touch with real life.

Maybe she did owe him a debt—for rejecting her.

Slowly, she came back to her chair. She sat down, facing him, and spoke quietly.

'I'll give you five minutes, Gerry, to tell me just why you came here. After that you're going.' She felt a sudden surge of strength, a feeling that she was in control at last. 'So—just what is it that's in your mind? Let's have no more play-acting, shall we?'

Gerry lifted his glass and looked at her, but she shook her head. He set the glass down again, sighing.

'You've grown hard, Cassa—you know that?'

'More sophisticated, I think you said.' He should have seen her this morning, she thought, in her Mickey Mouse T-shirt. And once again she wondered when Jet might come back. She still had a feeling she was going to need help in getting rid of Gerry Cornewell. She glanced at her watch. 'I said five minutes. It's four and a half now.'

He sighed. 'All right, have it your own way. But it could have been different. Don't say I didn't tell you that.' He fiddled with the glass, then gave her one of those quick upward glances of his. 'Look, I dare say you've seen the papers lately——'

'Not the sort you seem to feature in,' she said quickly. 'And I never, ever read gossip columns.'

He flinched. 'But you read the book?'

'Your so-called autobiography? Oh, yes, I read that.' She hadn't meant to when it had first come. She'd thrown it into the waste-paper basket, unread. But later she'd taken it out again, too curious to let it be thrown away. And she'd found the references to herself—brief enough, but sufficiently distorted to burn her with all the old shame, all over again. And yet there was nothing that was actually untrue—it was all done by implication. That was when she'd decided never to let herself get involved in any kind of biography again. Even the truth could be distorted, and only those concerned could understand the pain and humiliation that could result.

'Well, you know I've been a fool, then,' he said in the disarming tone that had been one of his charms. 'And never more than when I let you go. . . But just lately I've been getting involved with—well, let's say I've been flying a bit higher than usual. And I didn't quite see where it was leading—I always did let my heart rule my head, I'm afraid. And you can't afford to do that when you get mixed up with—well, let's say minor royalty. Actually——' he put on his modest look '—not so minor, as it happens.'

Cassa looked back at him steadily, unimpressed. 'So you've got yourself into some kind of hot water? And just how do you expect me to help you?'

Gerry gave her his rueful smile. 'Cassa, my darling, I don't *expect* you to help me at all. How can I, after all these years? But. . .well, I thought if you ever did have any feeling for me. . .perhaps you might *want* to—for old times' sake, as it were. Just come out with me a time or two—you know, be seen around. Let a few people speculate. That's all it needs to get me off the hook, you see. I can't actually afford this kind of—of talk at the moment. I need someone like you—someone who's not involved with my world at all—to make it seem as if—as if——'

'As if you're normal?' Cassa supplied helpfully. 'To get featured in the gossip columns with you—maybe even in the next part of your autobiography? And this will help you to avoid the scandal you seem to have got involved with?'

'Well, I wouldn't put it quite so crudely as that,' he said, sounding hurt.

'I would,' Cassa said cheerfully.

Gerry shrugged. 'Very well, if you must have it that way. Anyway, that's all I'm asking. Just come out with me a few times—I'll give you a good time, Cassa. You know the kind of thing—a few public occasions, Ascot, Wimbledon, a night-spot or two. I'll supply you with a nice wardrobe—which you won't have to give back afterwards. And in a few weeks you can come back to—what is it you do here? Do you work at all?'

It took you long enough to wonder about me and my life, Cassa thought, but she only nodded. 'I run a shop.'

'A *shop*?' He made it sound as if she ran a disorderly house, she thought with amusement. But perhaps he might not have been so shocked if she had said that. 'Well, you'll be glad to get away for a while. I take it you have an assistant? It can manage without you?'

'Oh, yes, I have a very good assistant.' Who is proving just how well she can manage without me, she thought, and wondered again just where Jet was and when he would be coming back. She'd been listening but had heard no sound from the stairs, or from the flat above. And she still wasn't sure that Gerry was going to be easy to get rid of.

'Well, that's all right. Now, what I suggest is that you come straight back to London with me now. Not to my flat, of course—I have a nice little apartment that you can use. A sort of company flat.' He coughed slightly and Cassa felt her lips twist. It wasn't difficult to imagine just what sort of 'company' he kept there! 'Tomorrow we'll have a look at the collection to see just what will suit you best. Remember Winterleaf?' He smiled, but Cassa kept her face blank and his smile faded. 'Well, I think that's all for now. I'll leave you to pack your things and make whatever arrangements you need to make, and I'll call for you first thing in the morning.' He was getting to his feet now. 'Anything you need to know?'

'No,' Cassa said. 'Nothing at all. Except——' Gerry paused and looked at her '——except just what makes you think I'm going along with this scheme of yours, Gerry?'

He frowned. 'I don't understand——'

'Oh, yes, you do,' she said calmly. 'You're just assuming I'm going to do whatever you ask. You think I'd jump through hoops for you, don't you? Just because I was infatuated with you for a little while nearly four years ago. Well, I'm afraid it's not like that. I got over my infatuation that night when you let me go just because you'd finished with me, because I'd served my purpose and was of no further use to you.' She stood up and faced him. 'I'm not going to help you, Gerry. And now will you please go? You've had more than your five minutes and I'm tired.'

He stared at her. His face was pale, his mouth tight. She saw a muscle twitch in his cheek. And then, slowly, he shook his head.

'Oh, no, Cassa. No, you don't. You don't refuse me. Because I can make you do this.'

'Oh?' she said, but a tiny finger of fear touched her spine. 'And how can you do that?'

'Quite easily,' he said, and there was now no mistaking the threat in his voice. 'Because I have a letter you wrote to me once, Cassa. A very revealing letter—more revealing than you know. Didn't you once tell me you'd been naïve? You wrote things in that letter that could be taken to mean quite a lot more than they actually did. It would make meaty reading in one of the tabloids. And there's no reason why anyone should know that it was written over three years ago. . .is there?'

CHAPTER SEVEN

As GERRY and Cassa stared at each other she heard the slam of the door at the top of the outside steps and then, as welcome as the sound of the US Cavalry thundering across the plain, the tread of Jet's footsteps.

How she knew they were Jet's she didn't stop to analyse—but whose else could they be? With a gasp that was half a sob of relief, she turned and ran to the door, dragging it open just in time to catch Jet arriving at her small landing before going on up to the attic flat. He stopped, his eyes widening at the sight of her face, and she only just prevented herself from hurling herself at his broad chest.

'Cassa? Is anything wrong?'

Behind her she could feel Gerry coming to the door as well, and she saw Jet's eyes go past her to look at the other man. His brows very slightly lifted, and then his glance returned to her face as he repeated his question. 'Is anything the matter, Cassa? Are you all right?'

Gerry spoke before she could open her mouth, his voice smooth and urbane.

'Of course she's all right. Cassa and I are old friends. Well——' the voice dropped into suggestiveness '—rather more than friends really, weren't we, darling? And we've just been enjoying renewing our "friendship", haven't we? In fact, we've been wondering just why we've been wasting so much time these past few years.'

Cassa gasped again and turned to him. He met her look, his eyes slightly narrowed, and she knew he was warning her. Ask Jet for help, tell him just what had been going on, and Gerry would carry out his threat. If only she could remember what was in that letter!

She looked back at Jet. He was watching them both, his face impassive, eyes like winter clouds. She could feel the dislike emanating from him in waves, and knew that Gerry Cornewell, with his silky sophistication, the rather 'precious' air he had cultivated, was definitely not Jet's cup of tea. But how could she let Jet know that he wasn't hers either? Or that she couldn't imagine now how she could ever have thought he might be?

In that moment, sandwiched between the two men, she saw very clearly just what it was she needed in a man: the core of strength, of integrity that she sensed in Jet—allied with a personality that was as lively as her own, as restless, seeking new experiences, treating the whole of life as a wonderful game; yet ready to settle down when he found his rightful place, and never too frivolous to understand that life has its serious side too. Sensitive as she knew that Jet was sensitive; able at times to relax into a perfect tranquillity, as she had already seen him do.

Jet was all these things and Gerry none of them. Yet there was one characteristic that they shared—that shying away from the ultimate commitment. And she felt the touch of sadness for the life that she and Jet could share so fully, yet never would.

'So everything's all right,' Jet said, his eyes still on Cassa's face. 'No problems.'

'No,' Cassa said in a high voice, 'no problems.' She sought desperately for a way to keep Jet there, to stop him going on to his attic flat and leaving her alone

again with Gerry. 'We were just having a drink,' she
offered in a tone that sounded over-bright to her ears.
'Why don't you come in for a few minutes?'

Jet didn't even pause to think about it. 'No, thanks,
I'm in rather a hurry. Off to see someone about the
book—I just came in to collect a few notes.' He gave
Gerry a brief nod and turned away. 'Nice to have met
you—er——'

'Cornewell,' Gerry said lazily, leaning back against
the architrave. 'Gerry Cornewell. You may have heard
of me.'

Cassa swallowed a laugh. Jet, heard of Gerry
Cornewell! Dior he might have done, or even
Hartnell—but *Gerry Cornewell*! She grinned as she
saw him shake his head.

'Sorry, can't say I have. But Cassa will tell you—I
don't move in the real world.' His eyes came back to
her face, unsmiling, cool. She was reminded of a lake
in winter. 'Anyway, I really can't stop to chat. Don't
want to keep my contact waiting.' He nodded again,
his glance passing over Cassa and Gerry as if they were
both total strangers, and bounded up the stairs, his
long legs taking them two at a time.

'How very *rugged*,' Gerry drawled, and Cassa was
filled with a sudden distaste for him. 'I'm surprised at
your parents leaving you alone in the house with such
a gorgeous hunk. Or maybe he doesn't turn you on?
Can I hope you still go for the more aesthetic type?'

'Like yourself, you mean?' Cassa's voice was tight
with scorn. 'Do you know, Gerry, I'm beginning to
wonder if you even know the meaning of being "turned
on". You're so in love with yourself that you wouldn't
recognise real attraction if it hit you in the eye. Let
alone love.' Her green eyes flicked over him like a

whip of contempt. 'Why don't you just go away and leave me alone? You must know there's nothing for you here.'

Gerry stared at her, his face hardening. He took a step towards her and she felt again that touch of fear. But he couldn't do anything to her. Jet was upstairs. She had only to raise her voice, to scream. . .

'You forget,' Gerry said silkily, 'that I have your letter. You really did bare your innocent little soul to me in that, you know. And anyone reading it might well conclude that you'd bared a good deal more.'

'I don't believe you,' she said, her voice shaking, and he smiled.

'It hardly matters whether or not you believe me. Unless you do as I ask—such a little thing, after all, for an old friend—you'll be able to read it for yourself. Along with several million other readers of the newspaper I have in mind.' He named the tabloid and Cassa gasped. The worst of what her father called the 'gutter Press'! Could he really do it?

'What good would that do you?' she asked, her voice dry. 'Surely it would do you just as much harm?'

'Not at all. It was such an innocent letter, you see. So charming. It could put me in quite a good light— show what a marvellous, considerate lover I am. You talk so much about my kisses, you see. And my generosity too. Oh, no, I don't think it would do me any harm at all.'

Cassa closed her eyes. He really did mean it. She wanted to call his bluff—to tell him to do his worst— but she dared not do it. How would her parents feel, to have her name, her letter, spread across the pages of a tacky newspaper? And she herself—she'd barely got over the humiliation of what he'd done to her before. In fact, she *hadn't* got over it—wasn't she even now finding it difficult, almost impossible, to learn to trust again? Wasn't that the basis of her problems with Jet? What would it do to her to have it all raked up again and exposed to public gaze?

'Petite dark-haired Cassie. . .' She'd had that long fall of dark hair cut away as soon as she'd left London in an attempt to cut Gerry away too. But it needed more than a physical change. She needed to change inside as well.

'So you'll think it over, won't you, darling?' The voice was soft, as soft as satin and as menacing as a snake. Upstairs she heard a door close, and her heart jumped. And Gerry heard it too. She felt his movement, felt him come closer to her rigid body.

'No use calling on the hunk, my sweet,' he murmured. 'In fact, I think we ought to make perfectly clear to him just what kind of relationship we have, don't you? Just in case he has any ideas of his own. . .'

And, as she heard Jet's footsteps begin to come down the stairs, Cassa felt Gerry take her in his arms and draw her hard against his body. Startled, shocked, appalled, her eyes flew open and she began to struggle. But he laughed softly, and the sound of that laughter chilled her bones.

'No fighting it, darling,' he muttered against her frantically twisting neck. 'Don't forget that letter. . .you *will* do as I want. . .' His mouth came up to cover hers. He was holding her in a grip far stronger than she would have imagined him capable of, one arm wrapped low around her back, the other hand holding the back of her head so that she could no longer twist away. Helplessly her hands reached for his shoulders, trying to push him away, her fingers digging into the fine cashmere of his jacket. She gave a stifled sob as his tongue forced its way into her unwilling mouth.

Jet's footsteps came on down the stairs, hesitated for a brief second as they reached the landing, passed and went on. She heard the slam of the outside door.

Gerry lifted his head and looked down at her. He was breathing hard and there was a glitter in his eyes. His teeth showed a brief, cold smile.

'Very nice, darling,' he said. 'You must have given an excellent performance. That desperate clinging to my shoulders must have been a convincing touch. And, with a witness to our passion, you'll find it very difficult to deny that our relationship is as intense as ever—won't you?'

Cassa stared at him. Her mouth was bruised, her body trembling. She felt soiled, violated. She would never want to kiss a man again—any man.

'Go away,' she whispered. 'Go right away. And don't—please don't—ever come back.'

Gerry laughed and moved towards the stairs.

'It's all right, Cassa, my sweet, I'm going. But I'm afraid I *will* be back. You're going to help me, remember? But I can wait a few days. No more than that, so you'd better make whatever arrangements you need to make for your little shop.' He nodded as if they'd just met in the street, and sketched a little wave with his hand. 'Bye for now, darling. See you again soon.'

Cassa watched as he ran lightly down the stairs, listened as he went through the door at the bottom. A few seconds later she heard a car start up in the drive, heard it roar away along the road. He had gone. He had actually gone.

Slowly, she went back into the flat. She collected their glasses and washed them, then looked again at

the one Gerry had used and dropped it into the waste
bin, knowing she would never be able to use it again.
Then she went back into the sitting-room, opened the
windows wide and lay down on the long couch, her
head back on the cushion that rested against its arm,
her eyes closed.

Her whole body longed to be held and comforted.
Her bruised emotions yearned to be soothed. She
thought of sun-warmed grass, of a rippling stream, of
kisses beneath a willow tree.

It all seemed a world away. But as she lay there she
knew that the one person who could comfort her was
the man who had held her in his arms only a day ago,
the man who had swept her away with passion and
desire, the man who looked up to see a herd of curious
cows and dissolved into laughter.

And who had seen her, only a few minutes ago,
clasped in an apparently passionate embrace in the
arms of Gerry Cornewell.

Because there seemed to be nothing else to do Cassa
got up the next morning and went to the shop as usual.
The thought of actually arranging to be away, of
complying with Gerry's demands, was an impossible
one—yet she couldn't quite see how she was going to
deal with the situation without getting herself into an
even worse one. If only she'd never written that letter!
If only Gerry hadn't kept it.

Letters, she thought ruefully as she unlocked the
shop door. They were nothing but trouble. It was
letters—letters written a hundred years ago—that had
brought Jet into her life, and letters that had created a
rift between them and made their developing relationship so fraught with difficulty. Whether they would

ever have managed to get anything going between
them was another matter—with Jet's Aquarian personality, that reluctance to make any sort of lasting
commitment, it might have been doomed anyway. But
at least the attraction between them could have been
given a chance.

Now, of course, any chance had been utterly
destroyed. After what he had seen last night she'd be
surprised if he even spoke to her again.

She went into the shop, picked up a few letters lying
on the floor just inside the door, and turned on the
lights in the display cases. The crystals gleamed up at
her from their black velvet bed and she stopped to look
at them, lifting the glass top to touch and stroke them.
Their smooth, regular surfaces were soothing to her
fingers; absently she handled them, lifted a few out and
laid them on the case of jewellery beside her.

She was totally absorbed in what she was doing, her
thoughts released from the treadmill they had walked
all night, drifting loose in her head, when the shop
door opened and Suky came in.

Cassa lifted her head and then went dreamily back
to her task. She had taken out seven or eight stones
now, hesitating over this one or that, selecting those
which seemed to call her, to ask to be chosen. As Suky
came to stand beside her she let her hand hover over
one more stone, touched it, lifted it, set it down
again—and then, at last, took it out to lay it alongside
its fellows. She turned to look into her friend's face.

Suky looked disturbed. Her eyes were anxious, her
face concerned.

'Cassa? Are you trying to do a reading for yourself?'

Cassa blinked. Her mind seemed to shift gear, the
drifting thoughts crystallise as if they were part of the

stones in front of her. Startled, she looked down and
saw that she had chosen nine stones, just as she asked
her clients to do when she read for them. Yet she had
set out with no such intention—it was always useless to
try to do a reading for oneself. It was as if something
had compelled her, as if the crystals themselves had
called to her.

'No,' she said blankly. 'At least, I didn't mean. . . I
just picked them out without thinking. But maybe. . .'
She looked down at the crystals, half fascinated, half
afraid. 'Suky, you read them for me. What do they
say?'

Suky gave her a quick glance. She looked again at
the selection of stones. Cassa could feel her reluctance
and understand it—they were close friends; Suky was
already worried about her—she wouldn't want to read
anything that might be distressing. And people who
understood the meaning of crystals could so easily
choose the ones they wanted to choose, and so distort
the truth.

But Cassa knew that she had picked these crystals
and gemstones out without thought for what their
meaning might be, as innocently as any uninformed
client might. If Suky could read them in the same spirit,
might not the future become a little less misty? Might
she not at least gain some insight as to the choices
which lay before her, some understanding of how she
should cope?

'Please, Suky,' she begged, and her friend looked at
her again and nodded slowly before turning her attention back to the stones.

'You're going through a difficult time at present,'
she said slowly, still with a trace of reluctance in her
voice. 'You're feeling rejected, unloved——' She

looked up, real distress in her eyes. 'Cassa, are you sure you want me to——?'

'Go on,' Cassa insisted quietly, and Suky turned back to the stones.

'Someone's deceiving you—there's someone in your life you shouldn't trust. You've been too trustful in the past and now. . . Cassa, I——'

'*Please, go on.*'

'You're anxious above love; you're afraid of it. Perhaps you had some past experience which set up barriers and now these barriers are holding you back. You need to overcome them.' Suky was looking increasingly unhappy, as if she felt she were reading a private letter, but she continued, her voice lightening a little as she read on. 'But it's going to be all right, Cassa. You're going to have a new beginning—a new home, even. And there will be happiness ahead; I'm sure of it. You'll get through this time and everything will be wonderful. Look—see for yourself.'

Cassa looked at the stones, laid out in the neat pattern in which she had set them. And there they all were, just as Suky had read them. The iron pyrites—fool's gold—which denoted mistrust. The variegated japser, which betrayed her anxiety about affairs of the heart. The turquoise of contentment and tranquillity, the agates, the quartzes, each with its own separate meaning, each so relevant to her present state of mind.

Too relevant, perhaps? Was she fooling herself about the way she had chosen these stones? Had her own knowledge guided her, even though she'd persuaded herself that she'd picked the different gems at random—and had she chosen those depicting future happiness simply because that was what she longed for?

Dispirited, disheartened, she turned away while Suky watched with concern in her eyes.

'Sorry, Suky—I shouldn't have asked you to do that. You're right—it doesn't work when we know each other so well, especially when I know the stones so well too. Forget it.'

Suky shook her head.

'It's not that easy to forget, Cassa. Look—there's obviously something wrong. I've been worried about you for days. Can't you talk about it? Isn't there anything I can do to help?'

Cassa shook her head. 'There's nothing anyone can do, Suky. And it's all too complicated to explain. I'll just have to work it out for myself.'

Suky looked at her.

'It's to do with that man, isn't it—the one who came in here the other day? The one you went out with?'

Cassa sighed.

'Partly. And partly nothing at all. It goes back years, some of it, and I don't know quite what to do. But there's nothing anyone else can do about it, Suky; it's my problem—so just leave it with me, will you? I shouldn't have involved you.'

'It's what friends are for,' Suky said quietly. 'And you've hardly involved me, Cassa.' She waited a moment. 'Well, you must do whatever you feel is right. But don't try to carry too much. Remember—I'm around if you need to talk. Or if you need anything at all.'

'I will. And thanks.' Cassa smiled at her friend, then turned away and began to replace the stones she had taken from the case. 'And now, how about a coffee before the customers start to flock in? I don't know about you, but I could do with one.'

Suky grinned and went to put the kettle on. And Cassa finished replacing the stones and closed the lid of the display case. There was a lot of sorting out to be done in her mind, she knew. Suky's mention of old barriers had brought the trouble with Gerry right back into her mind. She'd buried it for so long, but now she knew she was going to have to bring it out into the open and face it. And maybe a good place to start would be with that other reading—back in London, almost four years ago, when she'd never heard of crystals and what they could do.

But before she could even get her thoughts in order the shop door was opening, and Cassa, summoning up the welcoming smile with which she liked to greet her clients, was shocked to see a familiar tall figure darkening the doorway.

'Jet. . .' she said faintly, and he stepped inside, his silvery eyes fixed on her pale face.

'Cassa,' he responded in a cool voice, and as she sensed his remoteness her heart sank. 'I just called in with this. I thought you might like to have it at once—you might not have been going back to the flat at lunchtime.'

'Oh—thank you.' She took the airmail letter he held out to her. 'It's from Mum and Dad,' she added, knowing at once how ridiculous her words must sound.

'I just thought it might be,' he responded sardonically. 'It was the Australian stamp that gave me the clue. . . And did you have a pleasant evening?'

A pleasant evening with Gerry, he meant of course. And she shook her head at once, wanting him to know the truth. But Jet was drawing his own conclusions.

'No? How was that? Boyfriend have to go early?'

'He left only a few minutes after you did,' she said quickly. 'Jet——'

'So you were alone and palely loitering all evening. What a shame.' He didn't sound in the least sorry. 'Well, no doubt he'll be back. He clearly thinks a great deal of you.'

'Jet, it's not what you think. . .' she began desperately, but he froze her with a blast of ice from his chilly grey eyes. 'Jet, please listen——'

'I'm sorry, Cassa,' he said coldly. 'I don't think I want to hear. Your private. . .*affairs* are your own concern. They don't have anything to do with me. I think it's a pity you didn't remember your own commitment a little earlier, before we began to see so much of each other—another man might have begun to fall in love with you and got hurt. Fortunately I'm a little too level-headed and cynical for that to have happened to me.' He gave her a look that told her that whatever there might have been between them, growing as shyly and cautiously as a February rose, it had been destroyed now as surely as if by a winter's gale. 'However, I would warn you to take more care in future—you could find that sexy little body of yours getting you into real trouble one of these fine days. And there won't be anyone around to pick up the pieces then.'

He gave her a curt nod and turned to go. Cassa stood rooted to the floor. She wanted to run after him, to catch him, force him to listen to her. But she knew it would be useless. Jet Tayler had retreated behind a barrier too high, too dense for her to surmount, and he meant to stay there.

Barriers, she thought miserably, barriers wherever she turned. Barriers formed years ago, when her trust

in men had been so sadly damaged. Barriers erected
now, when she had begun to believe that she could,
after all, trust and love again. Barriers that everyone
put up to protect themselves from. . .what?

From pain. From being hurt. From love. From life.

How long does it go on? Cassa thought, moving at
last and going drearily on with the task she'd begun
when Jet had come in. Do we do it all our lives? Does
anyone ever manage to tear down all the barriers, to
look at the world with an open face and heart, to
accept love and pain as opposite sides of the same coin,
to understand that if you want to enjoy the one you
might have to suffer the other—and to count it
worthwhile?

How do they do it? How do they find the courage?

She looked again at the stones in their cases. And
she remembered her thoughts just before Jet had
arrived. She'd been thinking of that first reading, back
in London, after she'd run away from Gerry's apartment that night. She'd been thinking of her first
encounter with the magic of crystals.

It had been her flat-mate, Lesley, who had first told
her about the crystals. She had moved into the flat at
just the time when Cassa had first begun to see Gerry,
recommended by someone Cassa knew at college, so
they hadn't known each other well. And, with Cassa
being out so much during those first few weeks, they'd
barely had time to exchange more than a few words. It
was only on that last night, when Cassa had come in so
distressed, that they'd really begun to talk.

She remembered with warmth Lesley's solicitude
then, the caring way in which she'd seen at once there
was something badly wrong and set about making

Cassa feel better before asking even one question. Hot milk, liberally laced with brandy, a warm bath, the electric fire cosily switched on beside her as she sat, swathed in a soft dressing-gown, on the big, shapeless bean-bag; the lights low so that a tiny world, a haven of peace and comfort was created in the normally rather bleak room. . . Lesley had known exactly what was required. And when she had asked Cassa if she'd like to talk, there had been no curiosity in her tone, only a gentle invitation which Cassa could accept or refuse, whichever she'd wanted.

'I don't know. . .' Cassa recalled saying, and she knew that she'd felt the same then as she did today, as if she were enmeshed in a tangle from which there was no escape. 'If only I could see into the future. If only I could get some hint. . .'

Lesley was silent for a few minutes, then she said quietly, 'If that's what you really want, we could try.'

Cassa looked at her, half surprised, half laughing. 'What do you mean? Do you have a crystal ball or something?'

'Something rather like one.' Lesley had looked at her uncertainly. 'I don't know, Cassa. I don't know how you feel about such things. But I can divine— what you call see the future. At least, I can see the way your life is going, the trends that are uppermost. I can see the choices before you. It's up to you what you make of them, of course. I don't believe our destiny is all laid out like a road we've got to follow.'

Cassa began to feel interested in spite of her misery. 'You mean we can choose which path to take—but you can see what the paths might lead to?'

'Well, something like that, yes.' Lesley got up and went into her bedroom. She came out with a tray covered over with a cloth. 'These are my "crystal ball"—crystals, or gemstones.' She removed the cloth and revealed a pile of stones of all shapes and colours, a tumbled heap of well over a hundred different shapes. 'Do you want to try?'

Cassa shrugged. 'Why not?' It would pass the time, if nothing else. But she didn't really expect to gain any more from it than from her casual reading of the daily newspaper horoscope, glanced at and then forgotten. She bent over the tray, touching the stones, turning them this way and that, drawn to them in spite of her disbelief, and began slowly to make her selection.

Three quarters of an hour later she was staring at her flat-mate with a kind of half-frightened wonder.

'You seem to know all about me,' she said, her voice trembling. 'You know about Gerry—about what he's done to me. You know what sort of person I am. You know what's going to happen.'

Lesley shook her head. 'I know what *could* happen. It's up to you to decide what choices you make. You're in charge of your life—nobody else. Of course, I know you've been in love with someone—but I didn't know how that love was progressing, or that he'd treated you badly. All I can tell you is that you're probably going to leave London in the near future and start a new career. And that you've got a creative streak in you that you've never suspected—and that it could be psychic as well.' She looked again at the stones. 'And, from the extra three you picked out, that you will eventually be very happy. But that might not be for quite a long time. And you'll have to go through another rather traumatic time first.'

Another rather traumatic time. The words rang in Cassa's ears as if they had only just been uttered, here in the shop. She looked round, startled, as if expecting to see Lesley beside her, saying them again. But Lesley was far away, in America, where she'd emigrated to not long after that day. And, although they'd kept in touch, she had no idea of what Cassa was going through right now.

Or had she? Cassa had never been quite sure just how far Lesley's psychic powers extended. She only knew that she had learned all she could from the other girl, absorbing herself in the lores of astrology and crystals, meditation and divining. And, without seeing Gerry again, she had left London and come back to Malvern. It had seemed like the intervention of fate when she had found this little shop, empty and available for renting, and decided to take it on herself.

She had been happy, too. But she had never quite forgotten Lesley's words of warning—that there would be more trauma to come before she could be wholly happy. And before that she would have to face up to herself and her fears, overcome them and take full charge of her own life.

That time had now come, she thought as she heard the priory clock toll the hours, so close to the little shop. Once more she was at a crucial point in her life, and once more Gerry Cornewell was involved. But this time there were other factors too.

There was Jet Tayler, who didn't want a commitment. And there was her deep, unchangeable love for him.

CHAPTER EIGHT

STILL heavy at heart, Cassa locked the shop that evening and stood hesitating, wondering what to do next.

The warmth of early summer had evaporated, leaving a thin, cold wind that whipped at her skirt and struck through her cotton jersey. There was a lowering, inhospitable look about the hills that loomed above the town. She wanted nothing more than to go back to her flat, shut the door and light the fire. She wanted to draw the curtains against the rain that had begun to flick spitefully against her face, and create her own little world where she could hide and pretend that nothing was wrong, that nobody could hurt her.

And it wasn't until she was back in the flat, freshly bathed, wrapped in a long dark red robe and curled up on the long settee with a glass of wine in her hand, that she realised that what she wanted just wasn't possible any more.

It wasn't the sanctuary she'd imagined. It wasn't the haven she'd longed for. This little flat, the home she'd made for herself, furnished and decorated to her own taste that betrayed every facet of her personality—the peace of cool, tranquil colours in the sitting-room, the liveliness of a scattered assortment of cuttings and photographs pinned to the kitchen wall, the sensual femininity so openly acknowledged in the array of natural products and evocative essential oils in the bathroom with its delicate mother-of-pearl colour-scheme of apricot and palest grey—this little flat, which she'd wrapped around herself like a cocoon of security, was failing her at last. It was no more than the shell she'd often likened it to. And being in here now, alone, was like being on the top of the Malvern Hills with the cold wind that came all the way from the Russian Urals to strike into her bones.

A spatter of rain rattled against the windows, and Cassa shivered. In spite of the fire, she felt cold, cold right through. And she knew that what she felt was the ice of loneliness, eating into her heart.

Oh, Jet, Jet, her mind cried, where are you now? Why don't you come to me? Why can't you let yourself love me?

But he never would. He was an Aquarius man, afraid of commitment. No doubt there would be a woman, some day, who would persaude him to over-come that fear. But Cassa wasn't that woman. If she had been he would be with her now.

As had happened so often lately, her thoughts turned to the girl who had lived in this very house so long ago, the girl to whom Elgar had written the letters that had brought Jet to Cassa in the first place. Had she sat here, in this very room, her heart aching as Cassa's was aching for the love of a man who could never be hers? And what had happened to their love, if love it had been? Had one of them been afraid of commitment too?

She wondered what astrological sign Elgar had been born under. Aquarius, like Jet? But he *had* committed himself—he'd made and kept to a lifelong commitment of love with his wife, Caroline Alice. So maybe, if he had been. . .

As if that long-ago romance might be the guide to her own path, Cassa scrambled up and went to the bookcase to take out the biography of Elgar that her father had given her years before. It was an old one, written for children and giving little more than the musical details of his life, together with a few human touches about his dogs and his bicycle, Mr Phoebus, on which he had ridden about the lanes. But it gave his birthdate.

June 2nd, 1857.

So he wasn't Aquarius. He was Gemini—just like herself. Restless, lively, impulsive, wanting to communicate and doing it through his music.

Perhaps the girl had been an Aquarius, had drawn back from commitment. But it was unlikely that anyone would ever know that, unless they could find out just who she was.

Slowly, Cassa closed the book and laid it down. And, just at that moment, the doorbell rang.

Cassa froze. Who was it? Gerry—come for her decision, or rather the acquiescence he was expecting?

She didn't have to answer it. She could pretend to be out. Just sit here, quiet and unmoving, and wait for him to go away.

She heard footsteps mount the stairs. A knock on the door.

No, she thought. No, I won't answer it. He'll think I'm not here. All I have to do is wait.

Another knock. She clenched her hands in her lap, sat rigid.

Go away, Gerry, she thought. I've got nothing to say to you. And I'm certainly not letting you in here again. Just go away.

The knock was louder this time, as if her caller was

growing impatient. For goodness' sake, she screamed silently, I'm not here; don't you understand? Why don't you just give up and go away?

'Cassa!'

The voice was insistent, irritated. It was also deep—totally unlike Gerry's light, drawling tones. It brought Cassa to her feet, heart pounding, and then flying to the door. Before she had time to think she had the door open and was gazing breathlessly up into the eagle's face that looked unsmilingly back.

'Jet! I didn't know it was you——'

'Indeed? I thought it was precisely because you *did* know it was me that you were refusing to answer the door.' He was inside and making his way to the sitting-room without bothering to wait for her invitation. 'I'm sorry, Cassa—I know how you feel and I wouldn't have intruded, but I need an answer. And it seemed to me I'd better come and make sure of it before you disappear off to London and get caught up in your society life.' He was standing by the window, frowning at her as she came more slowly into the room. 'No doubt Malvern and your shop and life here will all seem very small beer when you're involved in all that glitz again. Not to mention my humble efforts at presenting a picture of one of the greatest composers England has ever produced.'

Cassa blinked at him, trying to make sense of his words. Disappear to London? Society life? Glitz? What on earth was he talking about?

'I'm sorry,' she began, 'I haven't the faintest idea——'

Jet snapped his fingers impatiently. 'Don't play the innocent with me, Cassa! I know exactly what you're planning. Haven't I had your boyfriend here half the afternoon, giving me chapter and verse? I must say, you had me fooled nicely.' There was an edge of contempt in his voice. 'I was beginning to think I might be getting you figured out—but no, you're as elusive as a rainbow; the second I think I've got hold of you, you're sliding away out of my hands and shimmering at me from somewhere out of reach.' His hands were clenching and unclenching at his sides and Cassa watched them in fascination, knowing that in his mind he was grasping her in those long, strong fingers. The thought brought a quiver of excitement to her body and she remembered the afternoon in the meadow, the surging desire that had caught her then, the ecstasy she had known in his arms.

'Jet——' she said again, but he wasn't listening. He went on, his voice now low and throbbing with frustrated emotion, now loud with anger.

'I suppose I was just a diversion, an entertainment to while away the time until *he* came back. Keeping your hand in, as you might say—it wouldn't do to get out of practice, after all. I can quite undertstand that! Just how far did you intend to let it go, Cassa—this dalliance of yours? And just how many others have there been, when you've been at a loose end without your glossy dress designer to keep you company? One for every night of the week, is it? Or do you have a rest on Sundays?'

Cassa stared at him. His words bit into her mind, into her heart, and suddenly she was filled with rage that he should accuse her in this brutal way. So he thought she was a slut, did he? Not only that she was Gerry Cornewell's mistress, but that she was so sex-mad that she had to have a string of casual bedfellows to occupy her when Gerry was away. All right, let him think just that, let him wallow in his bitter imagination, let him have even more to think about than he'd dreamed up for himself.

'A rest on Sundays?' she repeated. 'Oh, no—whatever makes you think that? I have two then, one before lunch and one after. Mind you, they have to be pretty special—not like the ones I go for picnics with in the middle of the week!'

The arrow went home with deadly accuracy, she noted with pleasure as Jet flinched. Why, he had actually gone white! Her pleasure was allayed with guilt and a touch of shame at having fed his jealous imaginings—and then she caught herself up on the word. Jealous? Was Jet really jealous? But, if so, that surely meant that he—he. . .

Cared? But—hadn't he made it quite clear that he didn't?

'Jet,' she said uncertainly. 'Jet, I didn't mean that— it's not true. But I honestly don't know what you're talking about. I'm not going to London.'

He threw her a look and then dropped on to the settee. 'Then why did he tell me you were?'

'He? Do you mean Gerry? He really has been here?'

'Haven't I already told you that? Of course he's been here! Giving me the once-over, summing me up as a potential rival. You can imagine I soon put him right on *that* score!' Jet's bitter laugh cut right through to Cassa's heart. No, he wasn't jealous; just angry. And maybe a bit frustrated too. Not wanting to be committed didn't mean to say he was never going to have any love-affairs, and he'd certainly been attracted to her. . . Once again she thought of the moments they'd shared in the meadow, their kisses on the hills, and her nerves tingled. Probably he'd thought that once he was here, living in the attic flat, he would have it easy. And, through her, get access to those letters he so badly wanted to read!

'So what's Gerry been telling you?' she asked coldly. Maybe it would have been a good thing to let Jet go on thinking she was off to London after all.

'Well, what do you *think* he's been telling me? That you and he had quite a thing going a while ago, that you split up after some silly tiff, that you came here in a huff and opened that shop to show your independence—and that now you're getting together again. He seems to think you're madly in love with him, and I assume he has reason to think that.' Jet's lip curled, and Cassa watched with a sudden sense of loss. If only that lip could have been curling around hers. She had a sudden yearning to be in his arms, pressed against his hard body, seeking his mouth with hers. . . But the way Jet was looking at her now, he wouldn't have touched her if she'd been Eve, offering him the juiciest apple in the whole of Eden.

'So Gerry told you that, did he?' she said quietly. She still wasn't sure whether it would be better to let Jet go on believing it—but her pride fought against the idea. She knew just what he must think of Gerry, and she hated to think what his opinion of her must be. And she hadn't made it any better with her wild admissions a few minutes ago. 'And you believe it?'

Jet flung her a bitter glance.

'Why shouldn't I? And if that's the kind of life you want, Cassa, well, who am I to say it's wrong? I just thought I was beginning to know you—the real you. Now I find I was wrong, that's all. Well, we all have to be wrong sometimes.'

Cassa caught her breath. She moved towards him,

letting herself down slowly on to the settee, staying at
the far end from him, keeping a distance between
them. Almost as if he were some wild animal she hoped
to trap—but no one would trap Jet Tayler, ever. The
slightest hint of a door closing and he would be away,
spreading those great wings and disappearing over the
distant horizon.

'Just what did you think you'd learned about me,
Jet?' she asked softly. 'What did you think I was like?'

His eyes moved to her face, then away again. The
bitterness in them twisted her heart, but he answered
with apparent honesty.

'I thought you were like a breath of fresh air,' he
said slowly. 'So alive, so full of joy, so thrilled with
life. As if it were a magic ball that had been created
especially for you. And yet you weren't frivolous; you
had your serious side. I admired your courage, the way
you stood up to me over those letters, even though I
believed you were wrong. But you did have a point,
and it was a point that made me think again about the
duties, the obligations of a biographer. And I admired
your integrity that wouldn't let you read them yourself,
even though you must have been as curious as I was.'
He paused for a minute and then added, so low that
she had to strain her ears to hear him, 'I wanted to
pick you up and put you in my pocket, Cassa. I wanted
to take you with me—all round the world—and show
you all the things I'd seen. I wanted you to see Alaska
and the Taj Mahal, Venice and the geysers of New
Zealand. I wanted to see them again myself, with you
beside me. I wanted to look after you.'

Cassa sat quite still, hardly daring to breathe. Surely,
for an Aquarius—for any man—this was a declaration,

a promise, a commitment? But Jet's next words shattered the world that had begun to build around her, brought it tumbling about her ears.

'I was mad, of course,' he said, almost conversationally. 'No doubt it all sounds most amusing to you. It amuses me now, as it happens, now that I'm over it. So let's have a good laugh together, shall we?'

'Jet—no.' Impulsively, she moved closer. 'Jet, I don't think it's funny at all. I——'

He turned his head towards her. His eyes, grey as smoked glass, moved over her, lingering on the soft curves outlined by the red silk of her robe. His nostrils flared slightly and she saw the darkening of his eyes. Instinctively she came nearer, her heart beating as she felt the warmth radiating from him, caught the breath of desire that she knew he was feeling even now, in spite of his words.

But her own fears were rising now to torment her. Suppose Jet were to give way to his desire and make love to her, after all that he'd said, with all the bitterness he was feeling? She could feel the tension in him, knew that he was on the brink of catching her in his arms, that once he touched her there would be no way back for either of them.

Part of her longed to let go, to entice him, to throw caution aside as she might throw aside her red silk robe. If she did that, might they not both find the world they sought? If they made love, might it not be like going through a doorway together, stepping into a new world, a world that was entirely theirs? Wasn't it worth taking the chance?

But something in her drew back. It was more than a chance she would be taking—it was a risk. And something in her shrank from taking that sort of risk, just as something in Jet turned away from making a commitment.

'You don't think it's funny?' he echoed. 'Perhaps it's just plain boring, then—is that it? Or maybe you just want to get rid of me.' His glance slid down over the contours of her body again. 'Maybe he's due here at any minute and you're just getting yourself warmed up for him, with your cosy fire and your wine and your slinky robe.'

Cassa's softness disappeared and she felt a spurt of anger. Why did he have to take everything the wrong way? Why did he have to destroy every hint of intimacy? He hadn't been like that in the meadow, when he'd held her and kissed her and murmured words of tenderness. He hadn't been like that on the top of the beacon, when they'd clung there together in the dusk. Why did he have to be like it now?

Perhaps her heart could have told her the answer if only she had been willing to listen. Instead, she moved sharply away from him, and her eyes blazed.

'You're determined to think the worst of me, aren't you? You haven't even given me a chance to tell you the truth, and you're not going to—because you don't want to hear it. You've made up your mind and you're not going to be proved wrong. Not the great Jet Tayler! And you talk about the duties and obligations of a biographer.' She tilted her face in disgust. 'Why, you don't even want to know the truth about living people, let alone dead ones——'

'Truth?' Jet broke in before she had finished speaking. 'You talk about telling the truth when you change your story from one second to the next? In five minutes you've told me you have a different lover for every day of the week and two on Sundays, and then——'

'I told you that wasn't true!'

'—you say there are no men in your life at all. And how you expect me to believe *that* when you were quite prepared to have an hour or two's old-fashioned slap and tickle with me down by the river one day and——'

'It wasn't slap and tickle!'

'—couldn't even wait to get inside the door with your old flame before you were practically melting into him the next. . .?' Jet floundered for a moment, having evidently lost track of the beginning of this sentence. 'Well, I just don't believe it,' he said at last. 'I don't believe a word of it. I don't believe a word you say, Cassa, and that *is* the truth.'

'Then I really don't know what you're doing here talking about it,' she said hotly. 'In fact, I don't know what business it is of yours anyway. Just why did you come here tonight, Jet? Can't you keep away from me, is that it? Because I'm wishing I'd never opened the door to you.'

'That makes two of us, then,' he muttered, and they sat gazing at each other, both breathing hard, eyes glittering, hands clenched. Antagonism sparked between them like summer lightning. Oh, how did we ever get into this? Cassa thought despairingly. And how are we ever going to get out again?

'Well, why *did* you come?' she asked in a desperation, afraid that they were going to sit there all night, until they became petrified and unable to move ever again. 'You must have had some reason.'

Jet blinked and moved his head slowly, as if he were coming out of a trance. His brows creased in a slight frown as he looked at her, and then he seemed to gather his thoughts together, to remember.

'Reason?' he echoed. 'Oh, yes, I had a reason. . .'
For a further moment or two he seemed either unsure
as to what the reason was, or unwilling to talk about it.
But at last he spoke again. 'Yes. . .it was the letter,
Cassa. The letter you had from your parents this
morning. I wanted to know—I wanted to know what
your answer was. If you were going to do it.'

Cassa stared at him. She felt as though the whole
conversation had shifted gear, taken an entirely new
direction. Letter? From her parents? What on
earth——? And then she remembered.

Of course! Jet had brought her a letter from
Australia that morning. He had brought it into the
shop. The postman normally left her mail on the stairs
just inside the door, and Jet must have found it there.
But why should he be concerned about it? How did he
know what was in it?

'Haven't you read it yet?' he asked her now.

Cassa shook her head. 'I'd forgotten all about it. I
must have pushed it into my pocket—I didn't give it
another thought. I've had so much else. . .' Her voice
trailed off. She couldn't tell him that her mind had
been occupied, partly by Gerry but more by Jet himself, all that day. She couldn't admit to the turmoil she
had been in.

'So you don't know what your father was asking you
to do?'

Cassa shook her head. 'No, I don't. And I don't see
why you. . . Oh!' Her eyes widened with sudden
illumination. 'Oh, yes, I do. Yes, I see exactly why
you're so interested. You know what's in that letter,
don't you? You know what he's asking me to do.'
Anger bubbled up in her as she jumped to her feet,
staring down at him. 'You've been speaking to him,

haven't you?' she breathed. 'You've told him about your book; you've asked him if you can see the letters. You've persuaded him to tell me to show them to you. And you *knew* he wanted to see them first!' Her voice rose as Jet too came to his feet, and she was forced to throw her head back to look up into his eyes. 'You just couldn't wait until he came home, could you? You just couldn't let him have that moment of pleasure.'

Jet towered over her. His face had darkened, seemed almost to have thinned so that it looked more than ever like the fierce, narrow head of a huge bird of prey. In his dark sweater, with his tawny hair springing in waves from his hand, he looked as if he were about to spread great bronze wings to overwhelm her. Anger seemed to double his size, and his eyes snapped fire.

Cassa's whole body wanted to shrink away, but this was one time when she wasn't going to give in to her fear. She faced him squarely, meeting his blazing look with a determined lift of her chin, her own eyes glittering with white-hot fury.

'That's what all this has been about, isn't it?' she blazed on. 'All your talk about friendship, about wanting to get to know me, about my being a "breath of fresh air"—my God, Jet, for a writer, you certainly have a way with clichés!—has been directed to this one purpose. Just so that you could get at those letters. And, when it didn't work, you started on my father. You got his permission to move into the attic flat and you worked on him over the letters. I suppose you got James to speak to him too, and tell him what a wonderful biographer you were, how you ought to have access to all the material available. Well, if he says that's what I've got to do, I suppose I'll have to do it. But I don't have to like it. I don't have to like you.

And, although I don't suppose it will matter one hoot to you, once you've got what you want, I may as well tell you now that I shall never want to see you again.'

She panted to a stop. Jet was watching her intently, his own anger no less, but when she finished speaking he gave a short, harsh laugh.

'Well, for a little 'un, Cassa, you certainly know how to use all your breath. I wouldn't have thought anyone could have kept going so long or so articulately as you've just done. Quite an achievement. Have you ever thought of applying for a job as a fishwife?'

'I'd have to marry the right person first,' she retorted. 'Have *you* ever thought of applying for a job as a fish?' And was instantly discomfited as he burst into sudden laughter.

'Well done, Cassa! Do you know, if I had to say what it is I love most about you, I think I'd say it was your quick wit?' He seemed to notice what he'd just said and hastily drew his face back into its sterner lines. 'All right, we'll cut out the jokes, shall we? You seem to have made up your mind just what's in that letter and what influence I've had on the writing of it. I suppose it's all that crystal-reading and so-called divination you go in for. Now why don't you read it and see just how right you are?'

'While you stand there ready to gloat? Oh, no, Jet. Whatever it says, it can't be that urgent—even to you. You're not going to finish your biography in the next few weeks, or even the next few months. Whatever's in those letters can easily wait a while. Why, you didn't even know they existed until James——'

'*But I know now,*' he broke in, his voice intense. 'Don't you understand, Cassa? Those letters were written while he was still a young man, before his marriage, before he moved to London and Sussex and then back to Malvern. What happened then might have affected his whole life. How can I write about any of that without knowing what was in them? How can I understand the man if I don't understand what happened to him at that time?'

'How can you understand him anyway?' she demanded. 'How can you know that those letters are so important—that there might not be other incidents, other relationships perhaps, that affected him even more? You see, you're just going to make assumptions which may not be true at all. You're like all the rest of them—biographers, journalists, gutter-Press reporters: you'll take a few facts and use them for your own purposes, use them as the whole truth when they're only a part of it. You can't *know*—nobody can!'

Her own situation rose up before her like a spectre. The threats Gerry had made, the way he intended to use her own letter written so incautiously years ago, when she had been young and naïve and believed herself in love. Suddenly unable to bear any more, she turned away, her slender body shaking as she fought and failed to defeat the tears. They fell like the rain that was pouring down outside, darkening the red silk of her robe, turning it black with their spreading damp.

'Cassa. . .' Jet was at her side, his hands on her shoulders, turning her towards him. 'Oh, Cassa, don't; don't cry, please, my sweet; don't for pity's sake cry. . .'

He gathered her against him, his arms wrapped around her so that she felt sheltered from all storms, his hands moving over her back in the comforting motions a father might have used to soothe his child. She felt the touch of his palms, slightly rough against the silk that slid over her skin, felt the sensuous friction of his fingertips as they touched her spine. She shivered suddenly and felt his body harden in response. And before she knew what she was doing, she had lifted her face to his, her lips softly parted, and looked up into eyes that were dark and wide, rimmed with glittering silver, as she had seen them once before, when he had kissed her.

And, as she had known he would, he kissed her now. He looked back into her eyes, and then bent his head to touch her parted lips and fasten his mouth closely upon them.

It's madness, she thought as the whirling darkness closed in upon her. It's utter madness—I'll regret it, I know I'll regret it. . . But such thoughts were thrust aside by the urgent pulsing of her body, the thundering of her heart, the singing in her head as she felt his lips shape her own, as she felt his tongue flick across their softness before beginning its invasion into her mouth. Strong, insistent, it explored every cranny with exquisite gentleness, then thrust with forceful and evocative movements against her own. It allowed no room for thought, but demanded its own response—a response that she could not deny as her own mouth answered his, as her tongue too began to explore, to reply without words, to touch, withdraw, enter, making its own quick, darting movements and then slower, stronger ones that sent their own urgent message. Oh, Jet, Jet, she thought as she clung to him, hardly knowing whether she was still on her feet or not; Jet, I love you, love you, love you. . .

He was lifting her in his arms now, cradling her against his lean, hard body, his mouth never leaving hers as he carried her to the couch. He laid her down as gently as if she were made of the most fragile spun glass, and drew slowly away from her, his eyes fastened on her face as with his hands he gently parted her robe and spread his fingers over the swelling breasts beneath.

'Cassa,' he murmured. 'Cassa, what have we been doing to each other? Wasting time. . .tearing each other apart. . .when all the time we could have been doing this. . .' He touched her nipples with delicate fingers, stroking them into a responsive hardness. 'And this. . .' He bent and took one into his mouth, his lips brushing the soft skin of her breast, his tongue moving against the nipple itself. 'And this,' he whispered, lifting his head, and laid himself alongside her, his fingertips running lightly, slowly tantalisingly down the length of her body, from the tender spot between her breasts to the even more sensitive area of her inner thighs.

Cassa gasped and twisted in his arms, but his fingers had already moved away, stroking down to her knees, finding the thin skin behind them, exploring down to her ankles and her quivering toes. And his lips were following, marking her body with little points of ecstasy as they lingered erotically in a way that she had never before imagined. It seemed to take him a long time to reach her toes, but it was too quick, she agonised, he'd moved on too soon, she wanted him to linger more, to kiss her again in just that way. . .but oh, the sensation as his mouth touched her instep, found each separate toe with the loving gentleness that he might have shown to a baby, yet with a vibrant undercurrent of passion that shook her to her bones. . . She reached for him, stretching her fingers out, longing for more contact, and tangled her fingers in the thick, eagle's-wing hair, felt his hand reach up and clasp hers, and clung to him as if to a lifeline. Jet, Jet, Jet. . . The name whirled through her mind, the sensation of his kiss, his touch, rolled in great waves over her body, and she groaned aloud in her need for him, her need for his love, his body.

Gently, he laid her feet on the couch and kissed his way up her body again, pausing only briefly to tantalise her before he was fully stretched beside her and his lips were once again on hers. With a muffled whimper Cassa turned into his arms, winding her own around his neck, pressing herself against him. There was no thought left now, only sensation, only the pounding desire of a woman for a man, only the urgent need for complete loving, for the fulfilment of the desire that had become paramount. Her mouth sought his, her body moulded itself against him, her hands moved and stroked and explored as his were doing, but they were hampered by his clothes. She found her way into his shirt and spread her fingers over his broad chest, feeling the thump of his heart within, but it wasn't enough. With a little moan of frustration, she tugged at his belt, and felt him laugh softly against her before he lifted himself away.

'I can see now that your stories about other lovers were completely untrue,' he murmured. 'I'll do it, or we'll be here all night—not that I don't hope to be anyway. . .' And his arms left her slowly, reluctantly, so that he could complete the task she had attempted.

Cassa lay still, watching as he began to unfasten the belt. And then, as she began to be aware of her surroundings, she heard a sound. A soft noise, as if from the door to the landing. As if someone were there—coming in. Or going out.

Her eyes flew to Jet's face and she saw that he had heard it too. His hands stopped. He gave her a quick glance and fastened his belt again, dragged his shirt together and strode to the door.

'What the—what the hell are *you* doing here?'

His voice was harsh and angry, and Cassa scrambled up on the couch, pulling her robe across her body, finding the sash and tying it with trembling fingers.

Gerry's light tones came from the hall, and the mockery in them chilled her to the heart.

'Why, I thought I made it plain this afternoon that I'd be back later. Cassa and I have a date—lots of dates, in fact. She must have told you that—didn't she? And when I found she'd left the door on the latch for me, why, naturally I came straight in. Don't tell me I'm interrupting something?'

He entered the room, his eyes dancing, and looked at Cassa as she stood by the fire, her body wrapped tightly in its dark red silk.

'Well, this *is* a cosy scene,' he drawled. 'All dressed up to go dancing, are we? Or were you just getting ready for my visit, darling? I always did like that robe, didn't I? So sweet of you to remember.' He came across the room and took her rigid body in his arms. 'It's all right, dear boy,' he said over his shoulder to Jet. 'We shan't be needing you any more. I can supply Cassa with anything she wants now.'

Cassa tried to step away, but his hands were like iron and the look in his eye was cold and cruel. She sent Jet a look of pure appeal, but to her dismay she saw that his face too was hard, closed, implacable. She thought of her behaviour on the past few minutes, the quarrel they had had, the things that had been said, and knew that he had reverted to his earlier belief and saw her as Gerry's mistress, as a girl who would take any lover rather than none, as a girl who would think nothing of

entertaining herself with one man while waiting for
another.

'Jet. . .' she breathed, but he was already turning
away. And she watched helplessly as he went out of
the flat without another glance, slamming the door
behind him.

'There,' Gerry said pleasantly, letting her go. 'That's
got rid of him. And not before time, if I'm not very
much mistaken. And now perhaps we can get down to
business. . .'

CHAPTER NINE

CASSA stepped away from Gerry. Her hands drew the dark red robe closely about her. Her face was pale, eyes glittering like a cat's below her tousled dark hair. She could feel her heart racing lightly, her body taut with the kind of apprehension that came to a diver who stood on a high board before a breathless crowd, a ski-jumper poised at the top of a fearsome slope, a parachutist in the moment before that leap into the sky.

'Get out,' she said in a voice that was like splintering glass. 'Get right out of here, Gerry.'

Gerry laughed. 'Now, my darling, you know you don't mean that. Not really. Oh, I may have interrupted a pleasant little interlude, but you know it could never have led anywhere. No future in it, sweetheart. He's not the type—even I could see that.'

His words cut through Cassa's anger and brought a shaft of misery to her heart. Was it that obvious? Was Jet's reluctance to commit himself plain even to Gerry?

But that wasn't the issue at stake here. Whatever had happened, was going to happen, ever could happen between herself and Jet, she had to get Gerry out now, and make sure that he never came back.

'That's none of your business,' she said coldly. 'None of what I do is your business, Gerry. Now—please go.'

He stared at her, his face hardening, and she noticed how pale his eyes were—the light, shifting blue of a puddle when the clouds had passed. Shallow, almost colourless. Untrustworthy.

The iron pyrites—the fool's gold—had shown her someone untrustworthy in her life. And she remembered the rest of the reading Suky had done for her.

The barriers she had to overcome in order to attain happiness. The risks she had to take.

'I think you've forgotten,' Gerry said in his silky, menacing voice, 'that I have a certain letter you wrote me once. An undated letter. A letter that could be very embarrassing to you. . .'

'I doubt it,' Cassa said coolly. 'Oh, you may have such a letter, Gerry, but I doubt if it will ever embarrass me. Partly because you won't ever get it published, and partly because I don't really care if you do. Nobody I know reads that newspaper, and if they did they wouldn't take any notice of it. They know just how accurate its reporting is.'

'When mud's thrown, some of it sticks,' Gerry said spitefully.

'And can be washed off.'

They stared at each other. Cassa could feel the thumping of her heart. Her ears were straining for sounds of Jet upstairs, but there had been nothing. Had he gone out again? Was she alone, here, with Gerry? She felt a flicker of fear and stamped it down angrily. She was *not* going to give way again!

'You've changed, Cassa,' Gerry said at last. 'You've grown hard. You're not the sweet, fresh child you used to be. It's a shame.'

'Life does that to people. It also helps them to grow up. You're right, Gerry. I'm not a child any more. I'm a woman. And you can't take advantage of me any longer.'

'Take advantage? Now look here——'

'That's what you did to me before, remember? Used me to make your mistress jealous, bring her back to heel——'

He laughed, but his laughter was uneasy. He was trying hard to keep control of the situation, Cassa realised, and she felt the sudden warmth of confidence.

'*I* used *you*? And who was it who had the run of my collection, who could pick any dress she wanted, who was taken to the best places, the swingiest nightclubs, the——?'

'And was shown off like a pretty doll, to be photographed and talked about and written about?' she cut in. 'And enjoyed it too—yes, I admit that Gerry; you did turn my head for a little while. But only a very little while. It didn't last long, did it—ten days, a fortnight? Just long enough to get a couple of items in the gossip columns; just long enough to bring Zelda flying back across the Atlantic. Whatever happened to her, by the way? Didn't she go back to Hollywood? I thought I read something about it somewhere. . .'

Gerry's normally pale face was suffused with a deep, flaming red. He took a step towards her but Cassa moved lithely out of his reach.

'You've got no hold over me now, Gerry,' she said, looking him straight in the eye. 'No hold at all. Go to your editor, ask him to print my letter in his grubby little rag and see if he will. I doubt if he'll give it space. There are so many much more interesting things to write about, after all, aren't there? Like your escapade with minor royalty, for instance.'

She had beaten him. With that last bold venture, with that last barb, she had beaten him. And he knew it. The shock in his eyes told her that he knew it.

Of course, he wouldn't give in without some more bluster. But Cassa could ride that, she could take it, knowing that the weapon he had thought so deadly had turned out to be useless—a paper sword, a wooden gun.

Eventually, his bluster died. His ranting voice faded and he looked at her in the cool room, and then he turned and went away. She heard him open the door to the little landing, heard the door close again. She heard his footsteps go away down the stairs and after a few more minutes she heard his car start up and drive away.

And she knew that he had gone out of her life forever.

For a little while Cassa remained exactly where she was, standing perfectly still. She felt as if she was waiting for the atmosphere Gerry had brought with him to fade away, allowing the tranquil peace she loved to steal back. Her room had been touched, violated. It needed cleansing, but only the wash of fresh, pure air could do that. And it must be done before she could go on and break down the next of her barriers.

It was her experience with Gerry that had set up those barriers, she knew now. Because of him she had retreated behind her own ivory walls, hidden her heart. She had never trusted any man since that night when she had seen him for what he was. She had been afraid of being hurt again, afraid to take the risk. And that fear had almost lost her the love she so desperately needed, the love that had come and knocked at her door and been turned away.

Almost? Hadn't she lost it completely when Jet had looked at her with contempt in his eyes and walked out of the flat? Had it ever been hers to lose?

Cassa moved at last, going over to the couch and sinking down on the soft cushions. She curled up, drawing the red silk over her bare feet, gazing into space as she thought of Jet's hands on her body, his lips on hers, the words he had murmured in her ear.

Had it been no more than a casual encounter, a dalliance? Or had it been more? Hadn't there been times when she'd thought he was making a declaration, about to make that commitment they both knew his nature shied away from? Even an Aquarian could come to it in the end, she knew, and, once made, it would be unlikely to be broken. That long hesitation was worth more, in the long run, than the impulsive promises that could turn out to be no more than pie-crusts, easily broken.

But I'll never find out now, she thought with a sudden bleakness. That really was my last chance. The way Jet looked at me, when Gerry walked in here, told me that he'll never try again. It's up to me now.

It was up to her to make the declaration. To take the risk. To open her heart to him—and to court a rejection more painful than anything she had ever known. And she felt herself shrink away from it.

'You'll have to go through another rather traumatic time first,' Lesley had told her. 'You will eventually be very happy.'

All she had to do was take the risk. The path was there, shown in the crystals—but the choice was hers. Her destiny lay in her own hands.

And what do I have to lose, after all? she asked herself. If I don't take the risk I've lost him anyway. It can't be any worse than that. . .

All the same, her heart was thumping as she slowly opened the flat's door and went out on to the little landing. And when she laid her hand on the banister and began to climb the stairs to the attic flat she felt as if she were climbing to her doom.

She had mounted two steps when she heard the door open. Jet came out on to the landing above her. He looked down and met her eyes. For a moment they both paused, and then he began to come down towards her.

'Jet——' she began haltingly, and at the same moment he spoke her name, in a dry, husky voice.

'Cassa——'

'Jet, I've got to say this.' She spoke rapidly, terrified that he would interrupt her, desperate to get the words out before everything could change again, before he could tell her he was leaving, before. . . 'Jet, what you saw with Gerry—it wasn't real, any of it; he was trying to blackmail me but it didn't work, it couldn't work, and I've sent him away now—and he doesn't matter anyway; it's you that matters; you and me.' She paused for breath, staring up at him with wide eyes, a kitten coming in from the storm. 'Jet, I love you—and I know. . . I know you don't want it, you don't want commitment, but I had to tell you; I can't let you go away not knowing. And that's why I let you kiss me and why I kissed you and—and—well, I just love you, that's all.' She came to a stop, her eyes on his face, then began to turn away. 'I just needed to tell you,' she whispered, and lifted her hand to cover her eyes.

Instantly, Jet was down the last few steps and had her in his arms. He caught her against him and she felt the lean, hard strength in his body, felt the powerful thud of his heart against her breast. She leaned against him, needing his support, feeling that she had come

home, that she was safe. . .and then she looked up into
his face.

Jet's face was dark with an expression she had never
seen before. It caught at her heart, drove the breath
from her body, set her trembling like a newly unfurled
leaf in a spring gale. For one wild moment she was
genuinely afraid. She saw him once again as an eagle,
a predator, hovering over her with talons outstretched,
ready to lift her and carry her to his eyrie. Just what
had she unleashed with her passionate declaration?
What had she set loose?

And then Jet did indeed scoop her up into his arms,
arms that were strong yet infinitely more gentle than
the talons of an eagle, and carry her—not to his eyrie,
but to hers, back down the stairs to her flat and into
the sitting-room where he laid her once again upon the
couch.

And he wasn't a predator at all, she thought as she
nestled into his shoulder. His arms had enfolded her
like the great protective wings of an eagle in his eyrie,
guarding his young. And what—who—would dare to
confront such a guardian? Who could hurt her, with
such protection?

'Do you mean what you just said?' Jet said, looking
down into her eyes, and she nodded. 'Do you know
what I was coming to say to you?' he asked, and she
shook her head. 'I heard him go—Cornewell. I heard
him leave and I couldn't bear it; I had to know if he
had taken you with him or not. Cassa, I was cursing
myself then—I thought I'd lost you, I thought you'd
left me, gone to London with him, and I knew that if
only I'd stayed with you there might have been a
chance. But the way he came in, the way he spoke and
went to you and took you in his arms—if I'd stayed I'd

have killed him. I swear I would. And maybe that's what I should have done!'

Cassa shook her head. 'He's not worth it, Jet. And he's gone now. He won't be back.'

Jet's arms tightened around her. 'I hope to God he doesn't, for all our sakes. And you'll have to tell me just what you meant by saying he was trying to blackmail you. But not yet.' His eyes looked into hers, dark again with that strange, heart-stopping expression. 'I've got something to tell you first,' he whispered. 'Something I've been wanting to say—oh, ever since the first moment I saw you, I believe. Certainly very soon after. All this time, every time I've seen you, every time I've held you in my arms.' He paused, stroked her cheek with a fingertip, touched her lips and then laid his palm against her face.

'Cassa, my darling, I love you and I want to spend my life with you. Will you marry me? Will you let this butterfly of an Aquarian take you off on his travels? Or do you want to make me into a pipe-and-slippers man? Because if you do—well, I can't make any promises regarding the pipe, but you can buy me a pair of slippers first thing in the morning and I promise I'll wear them every day if it will make you happy.' His voice shook a little as he added, 'Cassa, I'll do anything to make you happy. . .'

She gazed up at him and his eyes were almost black now, rimmed only with the tiniest band of silver. She recognised the expression on his face as love, love of a kind she had never experienced before, deeper and stronger than any he had ever allowed himself to display. And she felt a rush of that same emotion and knew that it was showing on her face too, a glowing joy that shimmered directly from her heart and cast an aura of brightness over them both so that the room seemed filled with light, and she could imagine the sound of an orchestra playing somewhere in the background, and knew that it was the singing of her own heart.

The film-makers got it right, she thought dazedly as she parted her lips for his kiss. There *is* background music. . .

It was much, much later, when they were sitting together on the couch, watching the light fade over the chequer-board of fields and hedges that stretched away to the distant horizon of the Cotswolds, when Jet asked casually if she had read her father's letter yet.

Cassa turned her head and stared at him. 'Dad's letter? No. . . I'd forgotten all about it. Jet, why do you want to know? Do you know what it says?'

He smiled a little, rather shamefacedly. 'Well, I think I do, yes. But, Cassa—let's be quite plain about this. I have never, ever tried to make friends with you—or anything more—just to get at those letters. Oh, I wanted to see them. I got James to introduce us—but the moment I saw you they shifted into second place. And whenever I've used them as a reason for seeing you they've been no more than an excuse. It was you I wanted to see, you I wanted to get to know all the time—you do believe me, don't you?'

She smiled a little, teasing him. 'I don't know, Jet. What about this morning—bringing the letter to the shop? And coming again this evening—you seemed very keen.'

'Keen?' He caught her roughly against him. 'My God, I was nearly frantic, especially after seeing you with Cornewell and hearing what he had to say this afternoon. He was so bloody plausible! And you kept drawing back; you'd never let yourself go—how could I help thinking you were just having fun? I couldn't even blame you—wasn't it the very impression I'd given you? Cassa, I seemed to get into a web there was no fighting clear of. I couldn't see any way we could ever come together, and I couldn't leave you alone.' He shivered. 'I even told myself that if this was love it was a hell I was well clear of—but I still couldn't keep away. I still had to come back.'

'And Dad's letter?'

He grinned. 'Why don't you read it?'

Cassa went across to the little table where the letter had lain forgotten. She slit open the envelope, drew out the thin sheet of paper, scanned it quickly. Her mouth curved in a smile.

'Dad can't wait any longer to see those letters—he's as curious as you. He wants me to have them photo-copied and the copies sent out to him in Australia. And he says I can read them myself, since it wouldn't be fair to me to ask me to do that without knowing what was in them.'

'And?'

Cassa looked at him with amusement. In spite of his protestations about the letters taking second place, there was a taut excitement in his voice. He caught her eye and smiled wryly. 'I'm sorry, Casssa. I can't help it—I can't help being interested. I'm a writer, a musician; Elgar's life is important to me at the moment.' He took her hand and held it in both his, looking intently into her eyes. 'Cassa, I intend to present as truthful an account as I possibly can. I don't want to distort the reality. It's the best I can do—and we do need to know about people like Elgar. Their *lives* can be an inspiration as well as their achievements, you know.'

Cassa nodded and looked down for a moment at their entwined fingers. 'I know. Those things I said—they were all to do with what had happened to me, with what Gerry did. I realised it earlier, when I got down that old biography of Elgar to check on his birthdate. I was ready to consult it when it suited me. She looked up into his face. 'Dad doesn't say I'm to show you the letters, Jet. His letter was written before he talked to James on the phone the other night, before he said you were to use the flat. But I think he would want you to see them. I think he would want me to decide whether to show you.'

There was a silence. Jet slid his arms around her and held her closely against him. She felt his lips in her hair.

'Thanks you for that, Cassa. It's what he said on the phone—but you came to it yourself, and that's something I shall always remember.'

They sat quietly for a while, and then Cassa gently withdrew from his arms. She stood up, taking his hand in hers so that he too was drawn to his feet. He looked at her with a question in his eyes.

'Where are we going, Cassa?'

She smiled at him. 'To fetch the letters, of course, and read them. Can you think of any better way to spend the evening?'

'I can,' he said as she led him from the room, 'but just at the moment I'm not going to tell you what it is. We'll save that for later. . .'

It was dark outside, the rain still streaming down the windows, when they laid the last letter back into its box and tied the ancient ribbons around them again. Cassa's eyes were wet with tears and Jet's face was tender as they looked together at the two little bundles. The lamplight fell softly on their faces, and the fire warmed them with its steady glow.

'What a nice man he was,' Cassa said softly, 'to have written all those letters to Lilian—his "Arum Lily". Did he ever realise she was in love with him, do you think?'

'Who knows? She was so young—he couldn't have taken it seriously, couldn't have believed it would last. But he never allowed her to feel rejected, did he? He was never anything but affectionate, never more, never less. He didn't raise false hopes and he didn't shatter them either. And yet it's quite clear that he was never going to marry her. She couldn't even have expected it.'

'Children do, though,' Cassa said. 'How many little boys have declared that they're going to marry their teacher when they grow up? And how many little girls have said they would marry a grown-up cousin or an uncle?'

'Or a favourite visitor to the house,' Jet agreed. 'As Elgar clearly was in this house. Perhaps this very room. . .' He lifted his head to look around, and Cassa knew he was feeling the awe she had often experienced herself, knowing that England's greatest composer had once played his music between these walls. 'And she was very young—eight, nine, no more than ten years old when the last of these letters was written. He couldn't have thought she'd harbour a passion for him for the rest of her life. And I don't suppose she did.'

'I don't know.' Cassa spoke slowly. 'I think she

might have done, Jet.' And when he looked at her, startled, she said, 'I knew her, you see.'

He stared at her. 'You *knew* her? Lilian Greene? The child who used to come here with her parents to spend her holidays—the child who received those letters?'

Cassa nodded. 'I think so. I'm sure of it. She was very old, of course—she must have been almost ninety when she died; I was about the age she was when these letters were written.' She got up and went to the window. 'She lived in a flat in that big house over the road—that window, the one with the light in it now, was hers. She would sit in it for hours on end.' She turned and looked at him, her eyes wide. 'Perhaps she was sitting there remembering—looking across here and remembering. But she never told anyone. I don't believe anyone ever knew that she'd been here as a child or knew Elgar.'

Jet came and stood beside her, his arm around her waist. They gazed out in silence at the big house, at the window where an old lady had sat remembering a past she'd never spoken of, remembering the man she had idolised.

'What a pity she didn't have those letters,' he said quietly. 'I suppose she thought they'd been lost, thrown away—and they were here all the time.'

'And she never married. She never loved anyone else.'

Jet's fingers tightened on her waist. 'No. We don't know that.' There might have been someone else—she was of an age to have had a fiancé killed in the First World War; she might have loved someone and lost him; she might not have been yearning for Elgar at all. We mustn't jump to conclusions, Cassa. She might

have thought of him as no more than a kindly uncle.'
His voice warmed with a smile. 'Didn't you tell me that
biographers must be extra careful not to put the wrong
construction on things?

Cassa laughed, and turned to bury her face against
his shoulder.

'I did, and you're right. We don't know—and we
never will.' She looked up at him, eyes shining. 'And
there's something else we'll never know, Jet—the
mystery of that piece of music. The thirteenth
Variation. The *Enigma* itself—the letters haven't
solved it at all. It's still a mystery.'

'And I hope will remain so.' He held her closely
against him. 'I agree with you over that, Cassa—it's
better left as a secret. As Elgar intended. But I'll tell
you one thing that isn't going to be a secret, not for a
moment longer than it has to be.'

'And what's that?' she asked, thrilling to the look in
his eyes.

Jet swung her into his arms. He carried her easily
into the next room and laid her on the bed. He slid out
of his clothes, and with his two hands he parted the
edges of her dark red robe. He caressed her breasts,
already swelling with desire, and laid his lips upon each
of them in turn. He lay down beside her and slipped
one arm beneath her body, lifting her towards him,
while his other hand moved gently, tenderly, with the
utmost delicacy, over her shivering skin, and his lips
sought hers.

Cassa turned willingly towards him, her lips already
parted, her skin softened by the anticipation of love.
She felt his mouth touch hers, brushing it gently as it
travelled over her face. Her hands moved over his
body, reaching up to the back of his neck to stroke the

short hairs at the nape, sliding down the firm line of his backbone. As if in response, his fingers moved down her spine too, finding once again that tender spot which had her moving, arching her back to come closer to him, a shiver running over her whole body. His palm cupped her bottom, holding her against him so that she could feel every contour, so that she knew his arousal and felt again that sharp tingle deep inside that denoted a quickening in her excitement, a longing and readiness for him, a yearning that this time must be fulfilled.

But Jet was in no hurry. His hand, that had been roaming in tiny circles around her body, over her stomach, down to the softness of her thighs, slid back to caress her shoulder and then down her arm to her elbow. He drew her arm away from his body, bringing her hand to his mouth, and began to touch and kiss her fingertips with the very lightest of movements, mere points of sensation imparted by the mobile tongue that then darted its way into the hollow of her palm, creating a burning flame of desire that scorched up her arm and back across her body, spreading and swelling as she twisted in his grasp, a fire that threatened to consume her entirely and in which she would gladly have burned for eternity.

'Jet. . . Jet. . .'

'Cassa, I love you,' he murmured, his voice deep and rough against her throat. 'I love you. I want you. I need you. I never realised what was missing in my life until I saw you—and then I knew that everything had been missing, always. You're my other half. We've got to be married soon—I can't risk losing you. I can't live with the torment of knowing you might get away from me!'

'I'm not going to get away from you,' she whispered

as she snuggled even closer against him, twining her
legs with his, wanting contact at every possible point.
'I don't think we're even going to get ourselves undone
from this knot we're tying! Oh, Jet—Jet. . .'

His movements were becoming increasingly urgent
as his hands moved over her body, seeking and finding
the spots where she reacted most so that she moved
and twisted against him. The outside world had disappeared, vanished, it seemed, forever; there was nothing
now but the two of them, skins almost melded together
in the heat their love was creating, nothing but the
desire that burned, the emotion that swept them away
on its tide, that refused to be denied any longer. There
was nothing but their world, the world created by their
passion, their love, their need. A need that had been
with them both since birth but could never have been
fulfilled until now. A need for completeness, for, as Jet
had said, their 'other half'.

And then, when she believed herself at the peak of
sensation, when her body had taken over entirely from
her mind and was responding in its own way, without
direction from her, Jet made that final movement which
would bring them completely together. There was a
moment of hesitation, a sensation of being on the
brink. . .and then they were as close as a man and a
woman could ever be, moving together in perfect
rhythm, soaring in unison to that topmost peak, the
summit where the air was rarefied, where only love
dwelt, and where at last they experienced together that
sunburst of emotion and joy that only true lovers could
ever experience, where they hung, poised, for a
moment, an eternity, before coming slowly, breathlessly, back to earth, wrapped in a glow that Cassa had
never before imagined, contained in a rainbow of

colour more brilliant, more iridescent than any that might have been cast by one of her crystals.

They lay for a long while then, at first quite still, then gently caressing each other. And even then, she found, it was not over, for Jet's caressing fingers took her to new excitement, to different delights, until she was as breathless as he, until she knew that she could bear no more and wanted nothing but to lie in his arms, relaxed, content, adoring.

'We're going to have such a good life, Cassa,' he murmured. 'But you haven't told me which it is to be— the Taj Mahal by moonlight, Venice on an April morning, the wilds of Alaska? Or pipe and slippers? Which do you want, Cassa, my darling? You can have anything you want, everything you desire.'

'I already have everything I want,' she answered, moving close to him again. 'But—you were going to tell me something. Something that wasn't going to be a secret any longer.'

'I was?' He looked at her for a moment, his eyes soft with the loving they had shared, and then he smiled. 'That's easy. It was the fact that I love you, of course. I was going to say that I would shout it from the rooftops. And so I shall.' He gathered her against him. 'Just as soon as I have the strength. . .'

Cassa laughed and nestled once more against his strong naked body.

'And you an Aquarius man!' she teased. 'Afraid to make a commitment, indeed! I'll hold you to that, Jet—I'll make you tell everyone. You're not getting away from me again.'

'And neither are you,' he said, and his hands caught her in a grip that made her squeal. 'You've slipped away from me often enough. This time I've got you— my midnight rainbow.'

STARGAZING

YOUR STAR SIGN: **AQUARIUS**
(January 21– February 19)

AQUARIUS is the third of the Air signs and is ruled by Uranus and Saturn. This is considered by many to be the sign of the future since the planet combinations result in a highly original character. As the Water Bearer, Aquarians may tend to show a rather cool nature towards others but, despite this, your bubbly nature means that you tend to make friends easily. However, others should beware since your highly individualistic nature may mean that you find your patience being tested when it comes to working closely with others.

Your characteristics in love: Aquarians tend to be rather wary of entering deep relationships although they often have many superficial ones. As a result, partners often need to display a great deal of patience. However, once an Aquarian has overcome his or her natural shyness and reserve, loved ones will be rewarded—an Aquarian in love is loyal, trusting and unlikely to deceive.

Star signs which are compatible with you: The signs of **Gemini, Libra, Sagittarius** and **Aries** all tend to be compatible with your cool ways while you may find that sparks fly if you choose partners with the characteristics of **Leo, Scorpio** or **Taurus**. Other signs may also be compatible depending on which planets reside in their Houses of Personality and Romance.

What is your star career? With their cool, logical ways, Aquarians tend to be brilliant at predicting trends and, while they tend not to be particularly motivated by financial rewards, it is often they who receive them! Aquarians also tend to be highly intelligent which may well suit careers in such demanding jobs as computing, scientific research, ecology and—dare we say it— even astrology!

Your colours and birthstones: As your sign is ruled by Air, it is hardly surprising that your birthstones are aquamarine or amethyst, both of which reflect your concise, logical clear thinking. You tend to also prefer pale colours such as blue which have a calming influence in your naturally hectic life.

AQUARIUS ASTRO-FACTFILE

Day of the week: Wednesday
Countries: Sweden and Zimbabwe
Flowers: Orchids
Food: Rhubarb, beansprouts. Aquarians often tend to find that food is low on their list of priorities—they are often too full of wonderful ideas in their heads to be concerned with their stomachs!
Health: Aquarians, with their intelligence and naturally busy lives, occasionally find themselves to be out of touch with their bodies which can lead to exhaustion. Plenty of rest, relaxation and frequent changes of scenery are necessary to keep you in tip-top condition!

You share your star sign with these famous names:

Vanessa Redgrave
Paul Newman
John Hurt
Placido Domingo

Marti Caine
Barry Humphries
Ronald Reagan

From the author of Mirrors comes an enchanting romance

PATRICIA MATTHEWS

Enchanted

Caught in the steamy heat of America's New South, Rebecca Trenton finds herself torn between two brothers – she yearns for one, but a dark secret binds her to the other.

Off the coast of South Carolina lay Pirate's Bank – a small island as intriguing as the legendary family that lived there. As the mystery surrounding the island deepened, so Rebecca was drawn further into the family's dark secret – and only one man's love could save her from the treachery which now threatened her life.

W●RLDWIDE

Accept 4 Free Romances and 2 Free gifts

•FROM READER SERVICE•

An irresistible invitation from Mills & Boon Reader Service. Please accept our offer of 4 free Romances, a CUDDLY TEDDY and a special MYSTERY GIFT... Then, if you choose, go on to enjoy 6 captivating Romances every month for just £1.60 each, postage and packing free. Plus our FREE newsletter with author news, competitions and much more.

Send the coupon below to:
Reader Service, FREEPOST, PO Box 236, Croydon, Surrey CR9 9EL.

NO STAMP REQUIRED

Yes! Please rush me my 4 Free Romances and 2 Free Gifts! Please also reserve me a Reader Service Subscription. If I decide to subscribe, I can look forward to receiving 6 new Romances every month for just £9.60, postage and packing is free. If I choose not to subscribe I shall write to you within 10 days - I can keep the books and gifts whatever I decide. I can cancel or suspend my subscription at any time. I am over 18 years of age.

Name Mrs/Miss/Ms/Mr _____ EP17R

Address _____

_____

Postcode _____ Signature _____

Mills & Boon

Next month's Romances

Each month, you can choose from a world of variety in romance with Mills & Boon. These are the new titles to look out for next month.

SUMMER STORMS Emma Goldrick

PAST PASSION Penny Jordan

FORBIDDEN FRUIT Charlotte Lamb

BAD NEIGHBOURS Jessica Steele

AN UNUSUAL AFFAIR Lindsay Armstrong

WILD STREAK Kay Thorpe

WIFE FOR A NIGHT Angela Devine

WEEKEND WIFE Sue Peters

DEAR MISS JONES Catherine Spencer

CLOAK OF DARKNESS Sara Wood

A MATCH FOR MEREDITH Jenny Arden

WINTER CHALLENGE Rachel Elliot

CASTLE OF DESIRE Sally Heywood

CERTAIN OF NOTHING Rosemary Carter

TO TRUST MY LOVE Sandra Field

STARSIGN

SHADOW ON THE SEA Helena Dawson

Available from Boots, Martins, John Menzies, W.H. Smith, most supermarkets and other paperback stockists.

Also available from Mills and Boon Reader Service, P.O. Box 236, Thornton Road, Croydon, Surrey CR9 3RU.